ECLIPSE

A Literary Journal

D0126368

Volume Twenty-Two Fall 2011

Glendale Community College

Glendale, California

ECLIPSE
A Literary Journal

EDITOR	Bart Edelman
FICTION EDITOR	Michael Ritterbrown

FICTION READERS

Shelley Aronoff · Claire Phillips
Mara Beckett · Piper Rooney
Ara Corbett · Kate Martin Rowe
Emily Fernandez · William Rosenblatt
Chris Pasles · Shant Shahoian

POETRY EDITOR — Bart Edelman

MANAGING EDITOR — Susan Cisco

EDITORIAL ASSISTANTS — Elena Grigorian, Arin Keshishian

BOOK DESIGN — Susan Cisco
COVER DESIGN — Greg Parks
COVER ART — Phil Shaw
Endarkenment
Limited Edition Print, 20" x 46"
Rebecca Hossack Gallery
London, UK

Eclipse thanks the Glendale College Foundation, Stuart Riddle and Melita Bauman Riddle, and the Associated Students of Glendale Community College for their generous grants. We also wish to express our gratitude to the Glendale Community College Board of Trustees, Dawn Lindsay, Mary Mirch, Ron Nakasone, Ron Harlan, Kristin Bruno, Rick Perez, Lisa Brooks, Paul Schlossman, Hbuk Bayer and Susan Cisco for their support.

Eclipse is a literary journal published annually at Glendale Community College. The editors invite submissions of poetry, fiction and drama. Manuscripts will be returned only if accompanied by a self-addressed, stamped envelope. Sample issues are $9.

Printed by McNaughton and Gunn, Saline, Michigan.

Glendale Community College
1500 North Verdugo Road
Glendale, California 91208

eclipse@glendale.edu

CONTENTS

Emily M. Green	Cold Front	7
	Going Under	8
John Davis	The Pack	9
Jean A. McDonough	What the Fallen Woman Knows	11
	Anything That Surfaces	13
Maw Shein Win	YOWL!	15
Christopher Lee Miles	What It Means to Pick Rock & Bale Hay	16
Leilani Squire	Khandar	17
Mary Beth Leymaster	Mother Load Rose	18
Patrice M. Wilson	Bone-Clock	28
Amanda Skjeveland	Fantasy's Limits	29
	Intimacy	31
Steven Winn	Couplet	32
	Name	33
Jeanne Hamilton	Going Home	34
Will Dowd	A Voicemail from My Father	36
	Fuel	37
Sandy Aragon	Insanity House	38
Tyler McMahon &	The Sweet Science	39
Paul Diamond		
Alice Jay	Sweater Girl	55
	The Silver Screen	56
R.T. Castleberry	Coupled	57
Linda Lancione Moyer	Moving the Pig	58
Gail Rudd Entrekin	Experiment	60
Joanne Lowery	Coin	61
	Arabesque	62
James Doyle	Archaeological Proof	63
Anny Edinchikyan	One Dance	64
Johanna Stoberock	The Strange Case of Ingrid P.	65
Catherine Johnson	The One Thing I've Never Told Anyone	71
Suzanne Roberts	What the Dead Sometimes Do	72

Charles Rammelkamp	Nymphomaniac	73
Ruth Thompson	Translations	74
	Bless You, Father Walt	75
Nick Conrad	Thunder	76
Azatuhi Babayan	Albatross	77
Joshua Ruffin	The Way My Uncle Smoked	78
Susan R. Williamson	Driving Back from the Antique Shop	80
Brian Keenan	Something from Nothing	81
LD VanAuken	Zombie Heart	94
Mary Carol Moran	Chambers Dictionary	95
Ross Talarico	One	97
Elena Karina Byrne	Bleach	99
	Crying	101
Jessica Stewart	Besotted	102
Gabriel Welsch	Make Your God an Ear	103
Bruce Douglas Reeves	MacBride with an "A"	104
Tom Chandler	Lascaux	117
Rachel Kann	Arboretum Canticle	118
Jed Myers	Where We Stand	120
Ashley M. Carrasco	Butterfly Within	121
Barbara Rockman	Soon, My Mother Will Die	122
Robert Guard	Grounded	123
	Heartland	124
Brad Johnson	Racist	125
Toni Fuhrman	Spoils	127
John McKernan	My Purchase of the Brooklyn Bridge	130
Tanya Stepan	If I Could Kill	136
Jim Daniels	Thaw, Freeze	137
	Desperation for Eternity	138
Ginny Lowe Connors	A Book, a Bird, a Question	139
	Wheat Field with Crows	140
David Hovhannisyan	Yankee Rose	141
Tyrone Jaeger	Woe to You, Destroyer	142
Ivanov Reyez	Leah	156
	Early Morning Coffee in Santa Fe	157

Maria Bennett	The Loss of Mathematics	158
	In Night All Is Passage	159
Nathaniel Doll	Alone with a Crowd	160
Lara Gularte	Mushroom Woods	161
	What Might Take Her Back	162
Bill Brown	The Little Blue Corporal	163
	This Poem	164
Larry Stein	Masks	166

CONTRIBUTORS NOTES   180

Emily M. Green/Cold Front

The summer heat gets pushed down to 50°,
leaves our tanned legs goose-pimpled. I think *our*
even though it's only me and my books
in our bed. I keep thinking I'm after their emotions,

but then I just jab the words for meaning, like a monkey
with a stick, working at a termites' mound. You can't miss
this about me—how I want one thing—but poke at another.
Maybe there's nothing you'll miss about me, or this bed,

or this city, which can't hold heat, even for a summer.
I should put on some pants, or a blanket. I should turn off
the phone's ringer, turn on the television, let the sound eat
through me. I should get good at forgetting. I won't

call you, tell you about the strange weather we're having.
I'll let the cold days pass. Take what the jet stream brings.

Emily M. Green/Going Under

Mykal and I dash naked over dew cold grass.
We jump far into her mother's pond. Splashes explode

like lamplight bursts on water.
We float on Merlot drunkenness, push

past each other and let out secrets,
each a firefly burnt out by morning.

She tells me that in high school, she throbbed
for comfort, so she lay in the bathtub,

feet on either side of the faucet, fixated
on the lick of water. She imagined

the shower massager as some boy's tongue
strumming inside her thighs. The water

ran her raw. I don't say that on those same nights
I was in the woods, lying on pine needles

jeans down for my boyfriend. My legs ached
and our sweat pooled on my stomach. Tonight,

I wanted to tell Mykal that as my lover came
and his face tightened, I conjured her, weightless

on the surface of the pond. But now,
as the cicadas and crickets compete

for attention in the darkness,
how small my desire appears.

John Davis/The Pack

I walk with dogs into the canyon of snow.
I ride inside their fur, become bits of ice.
These are the dogs who danced on the ribs of the earth.
These are the dogs who cried low moans of the wind up north.
These are the dogs who burrowed in snow and licked
their dewclaws until the moon rose.
These are the dogs who ran through my lungs, kidneys,
heart, ran off the edge of the horizon,
ran from the sunset where lava was stirring.

I am running with the dogs until there are enough stars
inside me to light the night's path home.
My days are growing warmer within the hoarfrost.
I am becoming the northern shadow moving on all fours.

When did I become the breathing inside a long scarlet tongue?
When did my withers warm the edges of a snowbank?
When did my blood begin to stain the glacial snow
1000 years old?
When did the dark spots on my flanks become ice melting?

We are running and turning the earth the way a hamster
runs and turns the earth inside his cage.
As we run our legs whisper against the snow.
The sound is recalling the first voices of the earth
and how mothers struggled
birthing the mountains, the sea, the layers of air.

The ghosts of our ancestors are rattling their bones,
keeping time with our running, tapping the rhythm
of the snowy egret's wings. And the rhythm cannot stop.
The lava is running out of the talus and scree

into our blood into our hearts up through the roots
wanting water up through streams and frozen waterfalls.
It keeps on rising keeps on layering the sky around us
which is the skin of the earth and we howl back
until the stars inside us begin to warm the moon.

Jean A. McDonough/What the Fallen Woman Knows

—after Marvin Bell

1.

A fallen woman is a woman who has fallen off
a pedestal, cliff, or curb; some say a fallen woman is
a woman who has fallen from grace. God's?
                              You can spot a fallen woman

by the sharp look in her eye; a fallen woman knows
the truth about a lot of things, like seduction, deceit,
betrayal. A fallen woman sees things clearly—
clarity is her burden.

2.

A fallen woman keeps to herself and usually lives
alone or with a small dog. A fallen woman may
not have family or may have family who refuse
                              to speak to her. A fallen woman

doesn't take any more risks; a fallen woman doesn't
keep any evidence; a fallen woman replays the events
of her life over and over therefore a fallen woman
knows herself very well.

3.

A fallen woman may only have one pot, one pan—no one
dines with a fallen woman. A fallen woman has no
visitors; a fallen woman is invisible, like a widow
                              who most people ignore;

a fallen woman lives with statements spoken
and unspoken, like I told you so, serves you right,
I'll pray for you. In time, a fallen woman may be forgiven
but she is rarely redeemed.

4.

A fallen woman may take up a hobby like knitting
or yoga. Most often, a fallen woman learns
how to mow a lawn, use a drill, manage a wheelbarrow;
                    a fallen woman has to keep in shape

because everything is hers to do. A fallen woman
might have to work two jobs to pay her bills
therefore a fallen woman could be called responsible.

5.

A fallen woman learns how to be alone on birthdays
and holidays—she cultivates a hard heart
nothing can penetrate. A fallen woman answers to no one
                    but the trees and open sky

appreciates her own backyard—a tall fence, small garden,
birdfeeder. A fallen woman takes notice of the small
things: the way a spider in an evening never crosses
a ceiling the same way twice.

6.

A fallen woman understands simplicity and keeps
few possessions. A fallen woman is expected to be humble
but she is too far gone for that. A fallen woman
                    is supposed to accept crumbs

of pity and feel grateful, but a fallen woman
who once risked everything for love would rather
starve than eat crumbs.

Jean A. McDonough/Anything That Surfaces

Any increased sensitivity to heat and cold?
a doctor asked—absurd because

this is the age I'm living through
not like when I was a child

and played outside in all kinds of weather
not knowing if I was hot or cold—my mother

the judge, checking my face for redness, feeling
my thin arms for chill. Under a maple tree

my grandmother in a wheelchair, a break
from the nursing home on a hot summer day

a delicate pink sweater draped around her
shoulders, feels cold, *she felt cold, she constantly*

felt cold, while the doings of a picnic accumulate
around her—Bobby, Bobby, she murmurs. *Who's*

Bobby? She watches my father at the grill
watches her grandchildren at play on the lawn

this is all she wants, to watch the way
I now like to watch my daughters

and their children: a baby on a blanket, a boy
on a soccer field, a girl with a flute—watching

is enough, I keep my distance, too. Under
another maple tree in my own backyard

still in my nightgown, I look up from my reading—
a bird glides into the yard to stab at the dry grass

and anything that surfaces, her sharp beak
a violent instrument. As morning nears

its end, it's getting warmer, time to go inside.
I am my own judge now.

Maw Shein Win/YOWL!

I saw the best cats of my generation deranged by hunger
stalking, maniacal, furry
prowling the alleyways and cul-de-sacs of Oakland
hunting for that abandoned bowl of Kibbles

feral felines, stoned on catnip, drunk on dirty rainwater,
loveless, lurking loners slinking through the dusky dawn
who arched their mangy backs, yowling under streetlamps
hissing, growling, leaping
mongrels and mutt cats   in heat

O felis silvestris catus! O animalia chordata carnivora!
O predator of hummingbirds!
reclusive panthers, mystical and alert
shedding wisdom and cat hairs,
fierce gods and goddesses of the otherworld

who collar-less and aloof pissed on the corners of San Francisco,
hallucinating sparrows falling from the sky,
sand cats, smoke cats, snap cats
contemplating paws

Christopher Lee Miles/What It Means to Pick Rock & Bale Hay

Life is a meaningless wonder. An inertia towards sweat. Think barn
    swallows
following the empty hay rack & tractor
to the field. The sky is more often gray
than blue. At least here, anyway.
Where torn T-shirts are ripped into oil rags
& stuffed in dusty milk jugs. The dust
more oil than grime, more grime than dust. A moist nimbus. Mute
    particle. As in cuticle: often viewed
but never seen. The blatant embedded
in our daily brain-fog. What lifts dissipates.
Then sinks into the prairie. Where limestones
crawl over each other to reach the surface & jut
out of the ground. They want to break your machinery.
Man needs something to pick. Why not rock? Why not
jagged ochre? Dim dust. Careless chink & chatter
as the stone crumbles. Kind of like poetry
only cleaner. Quicker to understand. Easier to
suck meaning from hot work than working
to understand hot.
                Back to the field where hay is binding in the baler.
Every ten feet the machine shears a pin. The swallows are silly,
almost drunk. They can't fly straight. Bellies filled with deerfly buzzes
& gravel dust. Think timothy seed. Think clover.
Think two shirtless boys waiting for their father
to replace the sheared pin.

Leilani Squire/Khandar

Upon the barren beach I rest your head.
The broken shell will whisper pools of gray
to stop this endless bleeding of the dead.

Our kiss, embrace still lingers on the stead
where arms entwine inside the starless day.
Upon the barren beach I rest your head.

The hopes of dreamy sea foam must be read
before the angels' moonlight crescent play
can stop this endless bleeding of the dead.

Once more I try but fail to reach love's bed,
an undertow is pulling night away.
Upon the barren beach I rest your head.

Again beat-beats the gunner's darkly lead.
Shroud, see the crying waves refuse to stay
and stop this endless bleeding of the dead.

When on the absent field of mist death fled,
ten devils stood amidst the tumbled clay.
Upon the barren beach I rest your head
to stop this endless bleeding of the dead.

Mary Beth Leymaster/Mother Load Rose

Mila rummages under the barbeque grill, locates the lighter fluid, douses her husband's socks, and ignites them, holding them out between thumb and forefinger. One minute too long and she's melted the polish on her index finger. Tossing them to the flagstone, she watches, transfixed, until a thread of smoke spirals upward, choking the air with roasted sweat.

The pink sock. Cheap, Kmart, cotton and neon pink, the kind of thing adults think little girls like. It was right over there, right beside the rhododendron, crumpled, with dirt caking the toes and heel like a shoe. Mud, really. If one of the cats hadn't been scratching and meowing, she never would have seen it, the way it was tucked under the bushes, behind the cedar bench. She has since ripped out the cedar bench and chopped it into firewood. She's thought about planting pansies there, right at the spot where she found the sock but if she did, she'd probably chip a nail. You can't be dredging in the garden, even with gloves, and not ruin your nails. Especially when you do them several times a day.

In the moonlight, Branden's socks twist like barbequed squirrels. Any human being with a teaspoon of compassion would stop leaving his socks out like this, where they cause nothing but misery, where they could lead an innocent bystander to discover what no person should ever have to find.

Mila locks the front door and for good measure turns on the two floodlights by the blue spruce. She's not the only neighbor who has her front yard lit up. Hesitating at the side window, she scans the street, searching for a darting shadow, a jogger perhaps, someone who shouldn't be there, or maybe, an unfamiliar car driving too slowly. Last month, she found it almost impossible to leave the house. Every morning, she scrubbed the kitchen table three times (not four, not five), triple-locked the back door, snapped off all radios, turned off the televisions, checked ashtrays for burning butts and candles for flames, returned all telephone receivers to their cradles, triple-locked the front door, walked out to the car, started the ignition, then scurried back, unlocked the front door, checked the stove and oven, the toilets for running water and ashtrays again for burning butts, then lathered and rinsed off her hands.

The leave of absence has been a good idea. She's relinquished the house compulsion and switched to nails. The zone of nails is hazy, safe, and driven. With color and brush, she controls everything: painted, polished and just the way she wants it. On a good day she paints them once. On a bad day, three times, maybe four.

She stands at the staircase for a moment, looking carefully at the darkened place under the stairs, the back door and alcove, then slowly makes her way up, one step at a time, noticing the lint collecting around the edges of carpet, around the railings where the wood needs to be dusted. But she just did her nails an hour ago and doesn't want to ruin the finish.

Branden sleeps like a drugged bull, his snore rattling the fringes of the bedside lamp. If she were in bed with him, she'd tell him to roll over to stop the noise but they haven't been in the same bed for months. Work shirts layer the chair, newspapers sit stacked beneath the window, pants shed in the middle of the floor. "I hate you," she says loud enough for him to hear, "Your own daughter could die on the front steps and you'd be snoring! Go on. Keep it up!" He's never been a person to take notice of much of anything, including the way their daughter Jen is shrinking before their eyes, bolting her door each night instead of coming down to dinner, refusing to watch television with them, or talk. Instead, Branden frets over things like fingerprint stains on the front window, hard water scum on the glasses that makes them look like they were never run through the dishwasher, ant mounds around the edge of the cement back porch, and the finger of holly that springs from the center of the bush like a cowlick that he keeps weed whacking off.

He arrives home, cracks open a Rolling Rock, grabs the remote, and waits for supper. He hasn't cooked anything in twenty-five years, just lolls. Sometimes he shouts, "What's that smell?" referring to the polish remover odor that permeates the house.

She stoops to pick up the pants and shirt by the foot of the bed and tosses them in the direction of the doorway. Beside the bed, on the floor next to his belt and keys, lies an overturned bottle, dribbling beer on her new carpet. Picking it up, she considers the possibilities. Raising it shoulder high, she tightens her grip and takes aim. She could jam it into the soft part of his skull and he'd never know what hit him. Might not kill him, but it would give him a good gash and a concussion. On television, she saw a woman jab a skewer into a man's ear. Certain death. "You were so cocky—you, chest-thumping *Big Man*! You were going to organize, put pressure. So, when—next year?" She lowers the bottle, positioning the lip against the bald part of his scalp, still considering it, rolling it around in a circle, caressing the soft spot. He doesn't budge but his snore changes to loud slurping noises. So easy. "If I have to fix everything myself, who needs you?" She finds a chip at the mouth of the bottle, a razor thin shard of glass that could cut, quickly, silently.

Suddenly exhausted, she slides the bottle into her pocket. Bending down, she gathers the dirty laundry at the door. "Picking up your crap isn't making it any easier."

Downstairs, she decides not to turn on the light, because then she'd have to see everything, the dust, the carpet needing vacuuming, the stains on the glass patio door. Besides, somebody could see in. Someone could be lurking just on the other side of the spruce, waiting for the right moment to slip from the shadows. Through the shade the moonlight is strong, slashing the room with light. It smells of the peanuts and potato chips Branden ate in the recliner while he watched television. Feeling around in the dark, she gathers the beer bottles from the coffee table and dumps them in the waste basket, stacks the magazines in the rack by his chair. Why does he drop his shoes and socks wherever he last sat? Especially socks. She kneels by the chair and feels around the carpet with her fingers, discovering a pair of toenail clippers, then the mound of clippings. The muddy shoes. The socks.

Next door, Ruth Kreider glowers over the back fence, clacks her false teeth and snips peony heads, pretending everything is normal. For the past two months, Lester Kreider has been using his weed whacker on every growing thing in sight, until his yard has started to resemble Kojak's head. Branden has begun a competition with Kreider and on weekends it's a pissing contest over the fence with weed whackers.

"They have doctors for this, Mom." Jen rattles her fingernails against the Formica. She doesn't paint them—they're peach-colored and broken. Only iridescent eye shadow and mascara interest her.

"I'll stop doing nails when you eat." Mila has noticed that Jen's hip-bones protrude from her jeans' pockets like knuckles, her ribcage forming a sharp ridge beneath the flimsy T-shirt, even though there's a small mound of flesh around her navel, which she pierced some time last month. What other body parts has she punched holes in?

"Medication." Jen peers under the lid of the shoebox, where Mila has neatly arranged twenty-two bottles of nail polish, all with black tops—only O.P.I. and China Glaze. One Revlon.

"On our property, Jen," Mila says. "A child from two houses away."

"Shit happens, Mom. The odds on this ever occurring again, here, in our lifetime, are a hundred million to one."

"You're too young to comprehend evil."

"Nails aren't going to fix it."

"Keeps me occupied. What did you eat, today?"

"Stop it, Mom. You need to start paying attention to the important stuff. Lots of things are going on right now under your nose." Jen shoves back from the kitchen table, the frown pulling her brow down like a cap visor. She tightens the band around her ponytail, the tip of hair swatting her shoulders. A row of studs glints in her ear.

Mila blows on her nail and frowns. "When did you get those things in your ears?"

"I'm leaving."

When Jen walks out, the kitchen feels enormously empty, like a warm bath that one minute is full of comforting suds and the next, has lost everything down a slurping drain. Mila doesn't know what she would do if she lost her child. You'd never feel safe again. Ever. Danger would lurk everywhere, a giant vortex, sucking out all air, swirling all good things into its cavity. That's how it would be. Mila listens to the faucet dripping, the stove clock that buzzes on the quarter hour, the hum from the strip of neon lights and, outside, the drum of Lester Kreider's weed whacker. The kitchen smells of spinach, olive oil, the afterthought of garlic. She twists open the bottle of polish and slides the brush down the middle of her clean, buffed nail.

Lizzie was five years old, almost six, a child Jen used to babysit. Slim and graceful, with soulful eyes. Neglected, yes, just a bit. Mila hated how she always had dirt smudges and jam around her mouth, crusts of sleep settled in the corners of her eyes. What kind of mother refused to wash her child's face? Mila remembers when her own mother used to spit on a handkerchief and swab their faces before they entered a store. Disgusting, smelling your own mother's saliva, but that's what careful mothers did in those days. Mila keeps thinking, what else didn't Lizzie's mother do? Was it her fault? Did she allow some stranger to stay the night, let him drink beer from their refrigerator, sleep between her sheets, when all the while he was listening for the sounds of Lizzie in the next room, maybe more attentively than to the clock in the hall, or the CD player, or woman sleeping next to him?

For certain, she didn't call the police when Lizzie failed to come home from school, not until ten o'clock at night. Why? It's made the neighbors eye her house suspiciously as they slink by, especially Branden and Kreider. When it's murder or kidnapping on national television, there's high drama and intrigue, with an eerie entertainment aspect but, here on their street, it has this awful surreal quality, as though poison is leaching pollutants and oxides into the lawn. Not a victim's house but a perpetrator's house. They blame her. She has a face—he doesn't. The rose bushes in front of Lizzie's house have withered, their branches not much more than sticks with thorns. Yellow patches corrode the lawn; branches weep like cobwebs from the fir tree. Crab grass strangles the mail box. The drapes are drawn. Lizzie's mother hasn't opened them in two months.

Mila discovered the sock behind the cedar bench, where the cat was scratching at it and meowing. It was the precise color of the rhododendrons. The sock, that color, is stuck in her brain but she knows it's a detour sign that takes her off the main road. The twisted leg, blood caked on her thighs, the smooth ivory body and naked pubis, with only the beaded bracelet around her wrist, the kind of thing a child makes in summer camp. Mila sank to her knees and placed her hands around the child's ankle. She looked, then looked a second time. A third. Her eyes couldn't adjust to what they were seeing. The meaning had gotten trapped somewhere, processed in the wrong place, like a key turning in a wrong lock. "No. Lizzie. No." She doesn't recall how long she crouched there, fingers clasped around the child's ankle, unable to decide if she should try to revive her, or pull her out. Branden slept like he'd drunk a case of Rolling Rock, even though she was screaming for him. She vaguely remembers touching Lizzie's cheek, and taking off her robe to cover her, not her face though, because her eyes were open. Gazing at something. Not surprised. Not in pain. Just open.

"It could have been you," she told Jen.

"But it wasn't."

"I'm terrified when you go out."

"Guess that's why Dad and Kreider cut down all the bushes, huh? So nobody can sneak in?"

"This isn't a joke."

"Everybody's a bunch of control freaks around here, trying to undo something that can't get fixed. No one's ever going to find him, so we're never going to know. That's how it's going to end."

Mila looked at her fourteen-year-old daughter, the flash of streaked hair, violet eye shadow and bare nails, not being cruel or jaded, just trying to hack away at the lies. But when you chipped away and removed everything—and you're forty, instead of fourteen—it terrifies you that there's nothing left.

Jen fingered the belly button ring, slid it out, and dropped it in the Coke can. "Let it go."

❖❖❖

Mila has pushed the dining room table close to the bay window where the light's brighter. Natural is better: it enables you to see small fragments of cuticle that might collect the polish, hangnails that need trimming, flecks of dust that can cause bumps under the first coat. This is the third time this morning but she still doesn't like the color: it's too red, blood red, and small fragments of polish have collected around the nail of her ring finger.

She sets out three bottles: *French Cognac*, *Madison Mauvenue*, and *Mother Load Rose*. All are good choices for fingernails but she has been considering switching to toes. She slips off her shoes and raises her foot. Her big toes have heavy calluses. On the second is a bunion where she's developing a hammer toe. Feet are more complicated. You have to soak them in the bathtub for ten minutes, then slather on foot scrub. By the time you've used the file and loofah, done the cleaning, it's forty minutes. She prefers the barefoot look—pink or pearly toenails like a child's. A child's. Bare, with the sock crumpled four feet away, Lizzie's foot was dirty, not soft and virginal but caked with something dark and thick. Maybe she'd been running. One leg jammed beneath the other in an unnatural position, the straightened leg scratched and bloodied as though one of the cats had run his claws down her flesh.

Mila smoothes the placemat in front of her and sets out the Nail Tech (for undercoat), the remover, and orange stick for correcting mistakes, Revlon Color Stay overcoat, and the bottle of *Mother Load Rose*. Seems fitting. Forget the feet. She doesn't want to think about feet. Squinting, she trims the cuticles of her left hand. Some say you should never trim the cuticle because it protects the nail bed from infection—but she likes the clean look, the way the skin curves like a satin frame around the glossy nail. In the shop, Andie says if she wants to cut back on hair and take on the nail work, she could make good money. One set of acrylics: ten dollar tip if they're satisfied. "I see how meticulous you are," Andie says, "You'd care more about these ladies' nails than they do."

Mila smears the Nail Tech II down the center of her nail, smoothes it out toward the sides, then slides the orange stick around the edges to wipe off the excess. Filling the Cutex lid with polish remover, she dips the tip of the orange stick in before easing it around her cuticles. She's still not sure she likes it. Still too red.

She catches sight of Branden on the other side of the patio glass door, watching her. Weed whacker resting against his hip, he stands motionless as a granite pillar, frowning, eyes set close together and blinking rapidly. No idea he is an almost-murdered man. Ignoring him, she finishes the left hand and waves it, blowing lightly. Twelve minutes for the first coat to set.

Branden slides open the door, swiping his nose with the back of his hand. Sweat has turned his shirt into a blotter, the stains spreading under his arms and across his chest, around the collar. He smells tangy, like salted orange peel. "Didn't you just do your nails?"

"As a matter of fact, yes. You'd know if you'd been up. But, apparently, that would be asking a lot."

"Are you practicing again? Did you decide to take that job?"

She shrugs and drags the brush back over the nail for the second coat, then under the inside of the nail, to form a protective coat to prevent chipping, a trick she learned from Andie. She holds out her hand to admire it. You have to be able to fix something in this life, even if it's mindless and insignificant. With a manicure, you start with a blank slate and the final product is flawless. Two and half hours. "You want something, Branden?"

Branden speaks through the opened sliding door. "You're starting to scare me. Talk to me."

"We could've talked last night but you went to bed at eight. I'm busy, now."

"Mila, maybe if you put your attention to something else. . ."

"Like what? Shaving the bushes until we look like a God damned cemetery? The whole block looks like a God damned cemetery! I'll know exactly when I need to put my attention to something else. In the meantime, I've got another forty-five minutes, here."

He balances the weed whacker against the glass door and rubs his hand on the rag stuck in his pocket. His face is sooty with stubble. "What do you want from me? I don't know what you're trying to accomplish, and I don't know what I'm supposed to do. Two strikes and I'm always out. Like you're some umpire calling a game I can't even follow."

"If you can't figure this out, I can't help you."

"Maybe he's somebody I know. Maybe he was looking for Jen. A neighbor. Or, a person we see all the time. A guy from Kmart, one of the stores. Somebody watching us, who got Lizzie instead of our daughter."

"The only answer is to find him."

"We've got to stop this, Mila."

She places the brush back in the bottle and twists the cap tight with a jerk of the wrist. She stares at the clock, then back at Branden, who looks angry and helpless as an abused child. Not the man she almost bludgeoned to death. She can hear the clock ticking, stretching out time, beating them both, stuck in this space.

"You want something to change? All right. Let's try this. It's five o'clock. Why don't you start by cooking us dinner? That would be new."

"I can do that." His voice sounds surprised, hopeful. "Just finish up here and put those things away. I'll get started." She notices he has grease under his nails.

❖❖❖

Mila places the nail box in the chest beneath the stairs. Taking the steps two at a time, in her open-toed sandals, she decides tomorrow she may do her feet, *Mauva Java* maybe, something in between innocent and hooker. Or, *Yucatan If U Want*. The odor of grease and eggs winds through the hall like low lying fog. Other than grilled ham and cheese sandwiches, it's the only thing he knows how to cook. It's going to be awful.

She raps on Jen's door and enters, knowing if she asks permission, Jen will say no. On the bed, her daughter sprawls in shorts and T-shirt, hands folded behind her head. She has no breasts to speak of. Did she, a few months ago? Mila can't remember.

Jen stares at the ceiling and adjusts her top, not quickly enough to hide the tattoo. Mila edges over to the bed. She doesn't recognize the red bedspread, which Jen must have purchased with her babysitting money. Hanging from the corner of the mirror are the rosary beads her grandmother gave her. They seem oddly old-fashioned, out of place. No one goes to church, here.

"I know what you're going to say and I don't want to hear it." Jen folds her arms across her chest.

"I don't know what I'm going to say, myself."

"Go ahead. I don't care."

"What?"

Jen starts to tap her foot. "Dad cuts bushes. You paint fingernails. Before—I wasn't scared. But I am *now*. You and Dad scare me." Tugging at the frayed edge of her shorts, face tight, she refuses to look Mila in the eye. "The only place I'm safe is in my room. I don't want to eat with you, or talk to you, or be with you."

Mila closes her eyes. How could she have failed to see this? It should have been so obvious. But there's time to fix it, isn't there? When you goof up a nail, you start over. It helps, really, to stop trying to be such a perfectionist, because you're likely, then, to make even more mistakes. Lots of times, just a relaxed flourish does it. Mila runs her fingers gently down her daughter's leg, stopping at the ankle. She curls her hand around it, comforted by the solid feel of flesh. "I promise, I'll pay attention now."

"Just no more weird shit." Jen sits up, grasps her mother's hand and spreads out the fingers, pressing them to the bed spread. "You're pretty good at this, Mom. I'm thinking you should go back to work. Andie needs you back there, especially in the nail end of things."

"You think so? Maybe. Could I practice on you?"

"No, I think you should just go back. Okay—one time. But nothing gross."

"It's a deal: I'll go back and you eat. We can start now—your father's cooking us dinner."

"I can smell it. Let's not make this *too* big. It's just eggs." Jen shrugs, "Okay—five bites. That's it."

Her daughter swings her legs over the edge of the bed, slips into her shoes, cheeks flushed, and twists the band around her ponytail. She smells like apricot shampoo and talcum. Mila places her arm around her daughter and together they descend the stairs, footsteps almost in rhythm but not quite, Jen's left hitting the step quicker than Mila's.

Jen says, "Lizzie liked her eggs scrambled with hot pepper flakes—you didn't know that, did you? Know what else? She loved me." Jen hitches up the shorts that are too loose on her, jamming the tail of her T-shirt into the waistband to cover her belly. On the delicate curve of her ear the studs glisten like tiny drops of moisture.

Branden is waiting for them at the bottom of the steps, spatula in hand, and Jen offers him an awkward gesture, just short of a wave. With a start, Mila recognizes that her daughter has her hands, the same long fingers, broad palms, and the thumb that crooks outward. *Silent Mauve* will be a good choice for the nails—pearly, same as the shadow around Jen's eyes. She'll like that. A little old for her years but with a certain air of innocence.

Patrice M. Wilson/Bone-Clock

It is ten o' the bone
and the heart's nightingale
is singing its last song
into the night.
Loud dust ticks in teeth
and tocks in the hot wet
manacle of the mouth.
The hour hand
gyrates at the wrist—
the minute hand pets the air
and pokes at the sky
in a hula motion
over the infinite sign
of your swaying hips,
while the second hand
pulses slowly
around an even slower
circle.

Come to me in an hour,
at 11 o' the bone,
come to me in the marrow
of the wickedest child.
We will dance into the wrong times,
the times that are neither
wrong nor right,
the body the only timepiece
that passes through night
without the harsh sound
of ringing in the morning,
without urgently crushing
the final silence
only it can know.

Amanda Skjeveland/Fantasy's Limits

I've taken a lover, studying the arc
of his broad hands as his fingers stroke
the keyboard in the bright white office lights,
so I'll know how to marionette them upon me
later when you and I make love in our shadowed bed.

I tease him until I'm able to etch upon the insides
of my eyelids his face flushed hot with impulse;
I shadow his kinetics until my collected parts
of him vibrate heavy and humid against me
and at the slightest thought of him I jolt.

I conjure his sounds, more guttural than yours—
he's more primal than you—and balance my life
against him, weighing us both, teetering
on the suspicion that given the choice
I would surrender all else I've collected
to sustain this apple at first pluck.

And in all my times with him
he feels and moves and sounds the same
and dulls with frequent wear. He speaks
awkward compliments until this sex
with him in the vast romance of my mind
becomes clichéd, so I grasp onto a first
we haven't had and while entangled
with you I hear him say he loves me.
I recoil at the manipulation, turning
away from you because my body follows
my mind as I turn away from him.

You ask what's wrong and cradle me close.
My make-believe fails in bettering your embrace,
so I curl up with my back pressed against your chest

because you are suddenly so warm and real
that I can't face you head-on.
I fold him up, as thin as tissue now,
and slip him away in a drawer.

Amanda Skjeveland/Intimacy

It isn't an easy birth, a simple trip to the hospital with rhythmic
contractions producing a child. I have had that kind, twice now,
totaling forty-six hours of labor pains. And the fear, and yes, the
    blood.

But this is different. The odds are better with that kind of birth,
not that things will always go well afterward, that a home will be made
and kept sacred by loving parents. No, none of those things are easy.

But society wants its bodies to reproduce, and the child won't stay
in its mother indefinitely, its ever-increasing weight restricting her
    arteries
while it kicks ribs and steals the best nourishment, so at least there
    are rules.

You and I unite in the dark hours of night and early morning to tangle
our emotions and minds, birthing precocious word-children who are
    only
as normal as our darkest depths, as saccharine as our grip on sanity.

They are allowed no social face, no lies to tell the well-armed critics
who will confront them. Yet we send them off, naked, to sit nervously
among the others. We are embarrassed for them—of them—even
    while

we remark on their progress, proudly identifying ourselves and each
    other
in their bodies, eyes, fear, courage. We embrace, watching, hoping a
    few
of our strongest will outlive us, validate us. What is more intimate
    than this?

Steven *Winn*/Couplet

Up in a tree
away from debris
  —Fragment of high school student poem
    Seattle, c. 1974

What might he have meant, that
unremembered bard, by this
goonily inspired harmony that's
clung to me where nothing
of Dryden or Sidney and
only shreds of Wordsworth do?

He intended nothing more,
I'd bet, than getting through
my class untouched or harmed
by beats or feet or stresses—
all those thudding things I must
have told him poetry employs.

And so he seized on rhyme's ballooning
rigor and rode it to an ether
realm where, sing-songingly, he
landed on a slim yet sturdy branch,
bouncing lightly above some swarm
of forlorn and blighted things,
all cares made musically carefree.

He must be close to fifty now,
and unless some later lightning struck,
likely had little more to do with verse.
But what a buoyant start and
tantalizing finish—a full career,
innocent, antic and consoling—
compressed into a couplet.

Steven Winn/Name

Steven not Steve, if anyone asks,
which normally they don't, deciding
for you what you'll be called, unless
it's some form or credit card transaction,
in which case the only issue is spelling.
"With a 'v,'" I reply, and that's that.

Once, before I had say-so, or thought so,
I was Stevie. Old birthday cards and
gift tags confirm it. "To Stevie—
Merry Christmas. Love, Mom and Dad."
And then for a while, and only between us,
I was Venner in my mother's soft voice.

The way Susan said it, heaving it
into my mouth when we fucked, I became
Steven for good. As is Susan&Steven.
Steven&Susan. Always the ampersand,
binding us together like a coiled coat
of arms until, after college, it unraveled.

Years later, before I stopped drinking,
I'd lean in at a mirror, at home, at a party,
bathroom locked against the clamor, and
speak it—StevenStevenStevenSteven
StevenStevenStevenStevenSteven—until it
was sound and a mouth moving, tongue and teeth,

eyes blanked, nose looming, breath clouding the glass.

Jeanne Hamilton/Going Home

I didn't cry
when my mother died.
I put on my coat and got on a train

for home. The Jersey flatlands
were covered with snow
and snow continued to fall

soft and silent. My father
was too stunned
to cry. The dog cried

for my mother.
He looked for her
all over the house

whimpering,
up and down the stairs
and up and down

again. Some neighbors cried
a little. They brought food
If there's anything we can do. . .

they said. We never knew
why
that day or any other day

why she turned her hand
against herself. She kept her
secrets clenched tight

seldom very happy
sometimes very sad and never
confiding. I don't remember

the funeral.
I don't know where the ashes are
or were after the flames

consumed the body
she had no use for.
We never knew

if she blamed me
or him. It was like reading a novel
with the last few pages missing.

Will Dowd/A Voicemail from My Father

The lawyer called and of course there's a problem
with my updated will, somewhere buried in it
is a split infinitive. If you remember the family legend,
all it took to abridge our ancient name was a distracted
bureaucrat thinking of what—a movie? a blonde?
Homeland and inheritance can be lost like that,
in a scribble. Now the infinite is somehow split.
How can I not take it seriously, whatever it means,
given the things I witness day to day? At the office
computers have died in my arms, reports vanish
at nothing more than a laptop's internal hum ceasing.
In Ireland, my father would grab a wild horse
by its neck, gripping and almost strangling it to show
his strength until it would break, just like that, in his bare
hands, the submission visible in its riveted eyes,
its even breath. The last thing I broke with my hands
was a printer. Now I handle its defiant jamming
with whispers, soft and importuning. The slogan
on my coffee mug is wrong. My desperation
is anything but quiet. It grumbles like bubbles
in the water cooler. All my father had to do
was get us here. Cross a single ocean. It fell
to me to learn the language of the land. Power
tools, credit cards, antennas, glinting discs, wires
in tangles, then no wires at all. It proved too big
a job for one lifetime. I couldn't keep up with the times,
the times that are now divided, split, separating what—
the years it took to get here and the years to come?
I heard a beep a while back, which makes me wonder
if this is still recording, or if it's only now recording.
However it turns out, you should know I gladly leave
it all to you, the million complications that stand
between us and the ends of days, the words
of this message. Save, reply, delete. Further options
unfold on menus I've never ventured to hear.
Do what you will, it's in your hands now.

Will Dowd/Fuel

You are not the first to wonder
       what fireflies feed on, nor to suppose,
in the lurid privacy of intuition, their need
       to drain the glare from a cat's eye
at night. But no, let's be realistic—

they're fueled by memories:
       that August night a tanker split its belly
and you go to see, expecting the usual
       dark-on-dark and still-warm sand, and find
instead an industrial stink, a viscid

lassitude in the tide—oil bridling
       the breakers. You turn your collar up
against slanted rain and do not see
       so much as instantly recall a barb
of lightning—and by then green

flames ribbon across the surf.
       Beds of kelp gone up like bonfires
heave onshore and light black fuses
       in the sand. In the absinthe glow
your pupils wince, then grow fat.

Sandy Aragon/ Insanity House

She's nowhere around,
working in the hopeless slate night.
You feel her cold presence
fill you up with sorrow.
Your soul shouts desperately for love.

Knives and plates fly across like shooting stars.
Pieces bouncing off from wall to wall dodging your tender heels.
Missed.

No one hears your helpless soul hiss at evil.
Your innocence slowly dies within you.
Turbid trip in that memory,
you stand alone, unwanted, and coldhearted;
poisoned by your hated, invective mother.

You rise broken by her insanity,
unable to think clearly. Chaos is in your home,
sweet home, where you learned to
aggressively torture everyone who
comes in your world.

Tyler McMahon & Paul Diamond/The Sweet Science

With his head still throbbing from last night's boxing practice, Thomas walked into his bedroom and dropped his suitcase on the floor. A small black boy he'd never seen before sat on the bed, playing Nintendo. The boy wore a woven cap that read "Sidekick" in gothic script. Thomas wondered if this was still his room. Was it possible he'd taken a wrong turn somewhere along the way?

"Can I help you?" Thomas asked.

"Naw," the boy said. "I'm nice." His eyes never left the screen of drifting hamburgers and French fries.

Thomas stared at the boy. The boy stared at his game. The game sang its song: a bouncing mechanical drone. For a sharp spiteful moment Thomas pictured himself strangling the kid. The image became too real, so he walked out of his room and lost the battle of wills that he'd scarcely pitched.

Thomas's father was diagnosed with Parkinson's disease last fall. Shortly thereafter, he became a born-again Christian at a boxing preacher's "ring-rally" in Austin, Texas. On the drive home, he explained his new calling: to save the souls of children from Washington, D.C.'s violent urban ghettos. At first, Thomas showed patience with his father's spiritual rebirth, confident that it would soon wane. But now, one year later, their house teemed with a dozen screaming eight-to-twelve-year-olds. The boys spent all summer digging through Thomas's drawers and closets searching for what they called the "booty kon"—a treasure chest of cash and dirty magazines that they'd convinced themselves was hidden inside the house.

In the living room, two older boys played checkers while a fat kid pressed random piano keys. Thomas shook his head and walked back out to his car. Halfway seated in the driver seat, he realized that his only peace in the past year had been inside this car, in transit between school and home, with one mess temporarily abandoned and the other yet to be encountered. He took his cigarettes from the glove box.

All semester, Thomas had spent his mornings copying *Walden* by hand—the assignment of his monomaniacal freshman composition teacher, Lisa. He spent his evenings at the gym, where upperclassmen pounded the crap out of him. That was his father's idea: join the university boxing team and build the character that comes from enduring pain.

He sat on the hood of the car and had a smoke. Lisa's pedantry haunted his thoughts: "You cannot fully understand America, without first understanding *Walden*." By semester's end, Lisa will have to read *Walden* twenty times in a row. She graded her students on the accuracy of their two-hundred-and-eighty page plagiarism. Out of the entire class, Thomas challenged the absurdity of this assignment the most. Lisa always offered the same two lines of defense. One: "You learn to write by coming to know good writing." And two: "You are free to tell the dean what I'm doing, but it will only get you a replacement teacher who will make you write persuasive essays." Thomas exhaled thin blue smoke and tried to ignore her.

Thomas's father emerged from the house. His hands trembled as he twisted the door knob closed. Thomas could measure the gradual worsening of his father's condition by his visits home. Was the old man's touch so unsteady when he filled cavities or extracted wisdom teeth?

Thomas dropped the cigarette onto the ground and stomped it out.

"It's good to have you home, son. Praise God." He placed a quivery hand on Thomas's shoulder.

On one side of the house, two older boys invented a game which involved bouncing a basketball off the exterior wall. It looked like an excellent way to break some windows.

"Are they all staying here through Thanksgiving?" Thomas asked.

"I have wonderful news." His father didn't seem to hear the question. "I sold the practice. I'm going to work full time with the kids."

"You gave up your practice?" Thomas was floored. "Dad, what you do with these kids is not work. Who's going to pay my tuition?"

"Seek ye first the kingdom of God and all other things will be added unto you."

Bible verses in place of conversation. Probity as response. Thomas cracked his knuckles.

"Dad, you could be off this Christian kick as fast as you got on it. And when it happens, you won't have a job. Don't forget: you've got your condition to deal with."

"Thomas, life proceeds out of your intentions for it. What are your intentions?"

"I have none. Life happens and I respond. I try to be decent along the way. That's all."

"If this is true than your life will be consumed with wandering."

"That's what life is," Thomas said, "wandering and wondering. And faith is wandering in credulity."

"Faith is accepting the mystery and going forth day by day in it." His father pressed harder onto Thomas's shoulder, as if testifying by osmosis.

"Have you heard from my mother lately?" They rarely spoke of her. She'd abandoned them both many years ago. It wasn't until now that Thomas wondered what life might be like with his other parent, wherever she was.

"Punch my hand." His father removed the palm from Thomas's shoulder and held it upright. "Let me see what that coach has done for you."

Thomas threw a weak right into his father's hand.

"Come on, step into it," his father demanded. "Believe in the punch. See it through or snap it like a whip, but don't enter with indifference."

"I don't care about punching anymore." Thomas threw another weak right. "I'm going to the store." He wanted to get in his car and drive around for a while, feel the enchanted peace that came with motion.

His father pulled a twenty-dollar bill from his pocket. "Could you do me a favor? We're out of milk. It would save me the trip."

Thomas wadded the money up in his fist and continued toward his Buick.

"Another thing son," his father added. "I promised I'd take one of the boys. He loves car rides. You don't mind, do you?"

The big-eyed boy with the "Sidekick" hat came through the door with his jacket in his arms. He climbed into the passenger seat, but said nothing as Thomas pulled out of the driveway and got onto the road. The boy stared out the window as deeply as he'd stared into the screen of floating hamburgers, his mind captive to his sight.

"I'm Thomas. Nice to meet you."

"My name Shug," the boy still stared outside. "What you doing at that man's house?"

"That man is my father. That was my room you were in, my Nintendo you were playing."

"How come we never seen you around here before?"

"I go to college. I live at school."

"What you study?"

"I don't know yet."

"How you can study if you don't know what you're studying?"

"It's easy. It's like right now: I'm going somewhere, but I don't know where yet."

"Ain't we going to the store?"

"I mean after I drop you back at the house; I'm running away."

"Where you gonna go?" the boy finally turned to look at Thomas.

"I don't know. I just decided to do it now. I can go anywhere—I can go into eternity."

"What's eternity?"

"It's just a word, an approximation of endless time. Nobody knows what it is."

"Take me with you."

"I can't. That would be kidnapping."

"Listen, Shorty. If you don't, I'll tell your father that you running away."

"All right then, Shug." Thomas saw no harm in it. "I guess you can come."

"Can we stop at 7-Eleven first?" Shug jumped in his seat. "I got a bunch of change from out your couch."

❖❖❖

They walked into the store with a cinematic sense of purpose. Shug picked up candy bar after candy bar, studying each one before dropping it back on the shelf. Thomas stared at a local daily newspaper in a black metal rack. Between two news stories, there was an eight-inch-long blank column, a dead space. On one side was a story about a kidnapped six-year-old girl. On the other side was a story about the new mechanical deer that the county was using to catch hunters who used illegal spotlights. Thomas kept staring between the two columns of text into the empty space. It was a complete mystery: Was it a story that missed the deadline, or perhaps some bit of news that had to be yanked from the press at the last minute?

Shug stood at the Slurpee machine filling a paper cup with colored squirts from each of the machine's chambers.

Thomas flipped through the papers beneath the one he was reading. They all contained the empty column, no headline, no byline, no story, nothing. "What do you think was meant to go in this space?" Thomas asked the man behind the counter.

"Probably about the football game that carried on pretty late into the night."

"What if it was meant to be empty to add some weight to the stories on either side?"

"Naw. That ain't how newspapers do things."

Shug hoisted a bluish Slurpee onto the counter, along with a paper tray of tortilla chips covered in layers of brown and yellow.

As they drove on through the grey afternoon, a potentiality ripped open in Thomas. Green lights, merging traffic, speed limit signs, roads cut through forests—these sights heightened his feeling that hope and peace of mind were the music not only of traveling but also of destination. But what was their destination? A green water tower stood against the horizon like a seedling growing suddenly to a mature tree. It rose to meet them, they passed it, and then it didn't matter anymore because it was behind them. On all sides, the fields were parsed up into brown rectangles. Thomas rolled down the window. The cold air passed through his hair. Wind thundered in his ears.

Shug finished his Slurpee and asked, "Where we going?"

"Where do you want to go?"

"I ain't never been outside D.C., 'cept to go to your house."

"You want to go to a pond deep in the woods?"

"Naw. They got freaks with chainsaws in them woods, and bears. I ain't going nowhere they got bears."

"How about Texas then?"

"Where the Cowboys play?"

"That's right. It's near Mexico, which means piles of steaming nachos. Cheese from the block, not the pump. Texas is like another country, the second biggest state in America."

"Why we can't go to the biggest?"

"That's Alaska. It's freezing, and full of bears. Texas is toasty and warm. Last time I was in Texas, I saw a bull that was so big it made normal-sized cows look like small dogs."

"I ain't never seen a bull. How come you know so much about Texas?"

"That's where we were last year when my father got saved and thought up his mission to save you and your friends."

"What he got saved from?"

"You know: a life of quiet desperation followed by eternal damnation. He's saved. He gets to go to heaven when his heart stops beating."

"Do bulls kill people?"

"No. Forget it. We'll pick another place. We can go anywhere, but first we need fuel."

Thomas pulled into a station. He turned to Shug. "You ever pumped gas?"

"Hundreds of times."

"Good. I'll use the restroom."

"Get me some candy!" Shug commanded while unscrewing the gas cap.

❖❖❖

When Thomas emerged from the bathroom, he saw a girl about his age behind the counter. She sat on a high stool, peeling an orange with long fingers. Bit by bit, she removed the white fibers, careful not to break the thin membrane that held in the juice. Thomas lost himself watching her. Without a sound, he placed a candy bar on the counter. She didn't look up.

"This and a pack of Marlboro Lights, please."

She said nothing. She put down her orange, worked the register keys, and retrieved his cigarettes.

"Oh! And the gas on pump number three," Thomas said. He wanted to find common ground with her. He decided to lead with the wounds of society: "It's a shame about that little girl who got kidnapped. Have you heard any news? Did they find her yet?"

She raised her head and looked him in the eyes for the first time.

His heart thumped.

"Yes. It's very sad." Her eyes were ponds that might have reflected a blue sky had she been under one.

"What do you think was meant to go in this blank spot?" Thomas pointed to the empty space in the newspaper on her counter.

"Eighteen dollars and fifty-two cents," she said and held out her hand, either not hearing him or ignoring his question.

He handed over his father's crumpled twenty and strained to come up with something interesting to say. This opportunity of a lifetime must be seized in this lifetime of opportunity. Those were his father's words, but they applied now as Thomas stood oafish and quiet while the narrow window of chance passed. Outside, Shug drummed on the roof of the car.

"I'm going to a mystery destination," Thomas said, "that's my Buick, and that little boy is my sidekick."

She looked impassively back.

"Why don't you come with me?" He meant it as a command, but it sounded more like the perfect set-up for a humiliating refusal.

"I can't leave work."

Thomas stood there for a moment with the change in his hand, then walked out the door.

❖❖❖

"Do you have a girlfriend, Shug?"

"I got hundreds of 'em."

"Hundreds? What do you do with a hundred girlfriends?"

"What you mean? You don't do nothing with them. You just have them. They your girlfriends. That's it."

Thomas lit a cigarette then handed Shug the Snickers bar.

"What they taste like?" Shug asked.

"Cigarettes? I don't know. They taste like smoke, I guess."

"Can I try?"

Thomas took another drag, then handed the burning stick to Shug. The boy made several attempts to draw smoke, and coughed violently after each huff. He handed it back to Thomas.

"They nasty." He unwrapped his Snickers and devoured it with relish, purging the smoky taste from his palate.

"What's your neighborhood in D.C. like?" asked Thomas.

"It's loud," Shug said without emotion. "And you can't leave no stuff outside, like you can at y'all house, no basketballs, bikes, or nothing."

"What about my dad? Why do you hang around him?"

"He take us out for pizza and stuff."

"What exactly do you guys do with my father?" Thomas suddenly discovered a curiosity he hadn't known existed.

"We eat. We play video games. He tell us about Jesus. Sometimes we do verses."

"He makes you say all those verses of his?"

"He don't make us. We just do it: First Thessalonians, five-twenty-fo'!" Shug raised the volume of his voice several notches, shifting into a rhythmic chant:

"Faithful is *he*. . .

"That calleth *thee*. . .

"Who also. . .

"Will *do* it.

"Brothers, pray for us."

Thomas stared at the hood of his car as it sucked up road like an old vacuum. Shug went through the verse again, with a deliberate accentuation of syllables, a catchy sort of cadence. Poor, sweet Shug, thought Thomas: lured like the rest of us by a world where he can eat nachos, drink Slurpees, and play video games. For a moment, Thomas questioned his journey in a larger sense. Maybe it was better to stay home and give thanks for junk food, a reliable car, and the other toys that grew lush in suburbia. Maybe he should be grateful to run errands for a confused dad. It was one imperfect father more than Shug ever had.

Thomas considered turning the big Buick around. He'd found a bit of peace now. But he couldn't swallow a humble return to those trembling hands and muttered praises. No, Thomas would drive until things changed somehow. He took an exit for a westbound freeway, and pressed his foot harder on the gas.

❖❖❖

Tires beat down upon the highway. Night fell over the land like a shroud. The road connected people to places to unfulfilled hopes. It did this in the movies. It did this in all the books Thomas had ever read. Now, it was doing it in his own small life. In the darkness, he could better appreciate the uncontemplated joy of driving fast.

Shug turned the radio knob past Christmas carols in search of other music. When he found a song he liked, he'd turn the volume way up. After a while he fell asleep. Thomas dialed the radio back to the holiday music and drove along in happy spirits. A news broadcast discussed the current issues that faced Walden Pond. The attempt to put a housing subdivision on the shore didn't interest Thomas nearly as much as the 75,000 bathers that visited the site each year. Because of them, Walden Pond now had the highest urine concentration of any freshwater body in America.

Shug woke up, yawned, and said, "I'm hungry."

"Me too," Thomas replied.

❖❖❖

The two smiled as they crossed the threshold into the redolent and well-lit shop. Thomas could smell donuts through every pore in his skin. Shug put his hand on his belly in a sort of benediction. Beiges, chocolates, and pinks were all laid out on stainless steel racks before them.

The donut man was bearded and full-bellied. His broad shoulders and heavy forearms made Thomas think that baking was an arduous physical task.

"What can I do for you boys this evening?" he asked.

"What do we want, Shug?" Thomas said.

"The holes."

The donut man turned around and Thomas read the T-shirt on his wide back: "If some things are absolutely bad then something has got to be ABSOLUTELY GOOD."

"What does your T-shirt mean?" Thomas asked.

"Read the front." The man pulled the shirt away from his chest. In cursive script it read: "If everything is relative and nothing is absolute, then why don't I take a gun and blow your head off right now?"

Thomas thought about the relation between the two sides. "I don't get it."

"It's the T-shirt of my band," the man explained. "We play Christian metal, a stigmatic metal. You might dig us."

"Maybe," Thomas said, nodding his head, letting the malapropism slide by. "Wait: what do you mean stigmatic metal?"

"We play music that sounds like the wounds of Jesus," the donut man answered.

"Yeah, I might like to hear that." Thomas mocked the man's deep, slow voice.

"Look." The baker pulled up his shirt. "These three scars around my heart are from three bullets that entered me from the front, passed through and exited here." He turned around and pulled up the back of his shirt to expose three larger scars—bald spots amongst the hairy lawn of his back.

"Wow," Thomas said.

"Yeah," said the man. "I told God that if I lived to see the next day, I would follow Christ to the word. I mean: that I would take the Word as it was meant to be taken."

"So, now you sell donuts?" asked Thomas.

"I got bills to pay. You boys from around here?"

"Naw," Shug said, "I'm from D.C."

"We're on a trip," Thomas explained.

"To where?"

"We're not sure, exactly." Thomas felt dissatisfied with his answer before he'd finished speaking it.

The donut man smiled as he placed the white cardboard box on the counter. "Well, I hope you get there fast. Anything else I can get you?"

"Chocolate milk," Shug said. "A big one."

"And coffee," added Thomas. "A lake of coffee."

"I tell you what," said the man. "If you're not heading anywhere in particular then you might want to check out Michael's hill."

"What's Michael's hill?" asked Thomas.

"You don't know? People have been seeing angels from that hill for the last six months."

"I ain't never seen an angel," said Shug. "Has you...what's your name again Shorty?"

"Thomas."

"Has you, Thomas?"

"No, never."

"I saw one last month," said the donut man. "It was an archangel, big as an oak tree. A lot of people have seen him. I got a picture while he was flying away."

He produced a glossy snapshot of a field and handed it to Thomas. Above the horizon of trees, an opaque white figure—arms outstretched—drifted with a blurred trail of movement. The angel was the size of a motel.

"People been seeing them day and night," said the donut man. "Where've you been?"

"At school," answered Thomas.

"That explains it."

"I wanna see the angel." Shug grabbed for the picture.

The man gave Thomas detailed directions to the hill—a series of rights and lefts with landmarks that they wouldn't miss even in the dark. It would be an hour-long drive.

❖❖❖

"We're on a mission from God," said Thomas back on the road. Shug filled his mouth full of fried dough. Smooth automatic transmission carried them further into the darkened rural routes. Now and then a road sign or a street light would fly past the low Buick. Thomas tore through the night, towards the supernatural evidence of God's hierarchy. He couldn't wait to stand on the hill, to breathe in the cold air, and let the stars play in his eyes. He convinced himself that over each horizon they'd find the next item on their list of directions. But around the curves and over the hills lay only more darkness and road. It was thirty minutes before they saw the first landmark, a Texaco station, where they took a right.

"What do coffee taste like?" Shug asked.

Thomas passed him the Styrofoam cup, a quarter filled with the lukewarm beverage.

Shug sipped it and curled his face. "Why you always be getting stuff that taste nasty?"

The next landmark was a tall radio tower with three flashing red lights on top. The early morning trip from school, the hours he'd been driving with Shug, it all caught up to Thomas fast. His eyelids grew heavy and his blinks lasted seconds. He saw tumbleweeds blowing through the shadows at the edges of his vision, which resolved into patches of disappearing fire. Figures of black lions lurked on the roadside. The illusions dissolved, flickered and changed in less than a breath. He knew he had to pull over and sleep, but he wouldn't. If he stopped moving, the frustration of the whole day, of the whole last year, would catch up to him.

To keep himself awake he relived the head blows he got last night in boxing practice. He pictured himself in the ring: globs of Vaseline on his cheeks, bulky gloves, skinny elbows, standing in his foolish fighting stance. Slinker hammered Thomas blow after blow with the colossal vitality of his ugly rage. Coach yelled: "Concentrate Racecar! Remember your slipping drills!" But there was no concentration at all in this sport for Thomas. The slipping drills went out the window as soon as the sparring began. Thomas could never move his head away from any punch before it landed. "Boxing is the art of timing," yelled the coach. "It's the sweet science. Throw one Thomas! Throw one!"

Thomas didn't throw a punch last night. He hadn't hit anything but a stuffed bag all year. He wasn't going to quit the team until he'd landed one blow. This meant conquering his fear and letting his guard down for the split second it took to connect.

Shug slept. Thomas's eyes grew heavier and he tried to remember those few lines that Lisa would always read aloud from *Walden*. He whispered: "Rise free from care before the dawn, and seek adventures. There are no larger fields than these, no worthier games than may here be played."

One dangerously long and lazy blink.

"The poem of creation is uninterrupted, but few are the ears to hear it."

Thomas yawned.

"I left the woods for as good a reason as I went there. Perhaps it seemed to me that I had several more. . . lives. . . to. . ."

His words and his attempt to stay awake trailed off as his eyes closed halfway. The two-lane road blurred into the dreamy image of a tent. The black tar formed a triangular opening between two flaps of earth on either side. The yellow lines were poles holding the tent up in the center. Thomas stepped inside to find a cot all made up for him. He lay down. His tired soul drifted off to slumber. He knew he had to stop sleeping, but he couldn't. There seemed to be an eternity in each second. Slowly an image came before him: it was Jesus, the risen. He was easily recognizable from all the statues and stained-glass windows made to represent him. On instinct, Thomas put up his guard and threw a left jab. Jesus dodged it then countered with a big right hook. Thomas breathed out as his head bobbed in a wonderfully timed V-slip. He stood there dumbfounded that one of his belabored slipping exercises had actually paid off. During this self-satisfied pause Christ reached out with two fingers and touched Thomas's unprotected forehead.

Thomas awoke, holding the steering wheel. He was flying down the road, still in his lane. His heart raced as fast as his mind. He'd been asleep for fifteen, maybe twenty seconds. He pulled onto the shoulder of the road. It didn't seem like a dream to him. It was the most real Christ he'd ever seen.

Shug woke up as the car tires crunched the gravel.

"Shug, you ever driven a car before?" Thomas asked.

"Hundreds of times."

Shug sat at the edge of the driver's seat. His short legs just reached to the acceleration and brake pedals. He could barely see over the wheel. The car left the shoulder. A passenger now, Thomas was consumed by what had happened. This vision had to be absorbed and understood while it was fresh. Christ offered something with that touch: fullness of time, depth of spirit, messianic essence. And Thomas's first reaction was to punch.

Shug was a talkative driver. He kept saying: "Yeah, Shorty! I'm geggin' it now! And look out: I been drinking!"

The first time Shug saw headlights come toward him he began muttering the word, "iggity," slowly at first, and then more and more rapidly as the lights got closer "iggity, iggity, gitygity" until the nonsense words came out truncated, quickly. The lights passed, and he went quiet until the next car approached.

Shug began again: "iggity, iggity." But this time, there was no other set of headlights. It was a doe frozen in the high beams. And Shug didn't slow down. He held his lane, saying "iggity" faster. The deer wavered tragically. Thomas's heart surged. Shug steered the Buick into the grass, around the beast and back on the road, without over or under steering an inch, as though he'd done it a hundred times.

"That was a tremendous feat of driving," Thomas said. "Most people would have skidded right into that thing."

"Naw, it weren't nothing. It's just like the *Back Roads Driving* game at Pizza Hut. The deer gonna go one of two ways; you just got to make a move as soon as it does."

"But that deer didn't make a move."

"If it don't move," Shug said, "then you go around it."

Soon they saw the blinking red lights of the tower. Shug made the turn and continued to the next landmark, a white church. They were nearing the hill when a buck stepped into the road just ahead of them. Shug let off the gas and steered into the shoulder. The buck also turned back to the shoulder.

After the collision, Shug's body was wedged between the windscreen and the dash. The buck brought the car to a standstill. Thomas pulled Shug out and checked him for blood and sore spots. The boy was shaken but not hurt. Thomas wiped at his perspiring forehead and noticed that it was bleeding.

A hairy, bloody, hoofed carcass lay about ten yards in front of the car. Thomas took several steps toward it. He felt sick looking at the graceful beast. He turned back to the car: the hood was folded inward, the bumper gone, headlights shattered, radiator in the gravel, blood and fur on the fan, and little Shug crying inside.

"It's okay," said Thomas. "We're both okay. Come outside and take a walk with me."

"We gonna get eaten by bears!" Shug sobbed.

"There are no bears in this part of the country."

"How you know?" said Shug through tears.

"I promise you," said Thomas pulling him out of the car. "I've never seen a bear around here in all my life."

"You know where we are?" Shug asked.

"No," Thomas admitted.

Shug cried more and wiped his face with his coat sleeve. They stepped out onto the road's shoulder. The gravel crunched underfoot, and the stars burned bright overhead. The angels remained—as always—just out of sight, and silence was what there was to share for a while.

"Your head bleeding," Shug said.

"I know."

"But it's bad. It's all down your face and junk."

"I don't care."

"I care. Bears can smell blood from miles away!"

"You're thinking of sharks."

"I'm talking 'bout bears!"

"Who told you that?"

"I just know it. It's a fact of the wild. We in the wild, right?"

"No. We're on a dark road between two empty fields."

Shug ran to the car.

Thomas followed and locked the doors.

"Look Shug, I'm having a cigarette. Why don't you have one? They take away fear. That's why people smoke them." Thomas hoped that conspiring in self-destructive behavior might bring a temporary peace between them.

"They got wild turkeys out here?" Shug asked.

"I suppose so," Thomas said.

"Do turkeys kill people?"

"Nothing is going to hurt you, Shug. Smoke one of these. You won't be afraid."

Thomas lit his cigarette. Shug kept his unlit between his lips. After the smoke, Thomas leaned his seat back and said, "I'm going to sleep."

Shug looked out the window while the stars slowly rotated above.

Thomas slept deeply and dreamed that he was the doubting Thomas, but when the resurrected Christ allowed him to put his hand in the wounded side, Thomas didn't stop there. He reached his whole arm in, up to the elbow, feeling around, over Christ's beating heart, reaching still further, up to the shoulder. He meant to duck his head and crawl inside the savior's body. But then the smell turned from fragrant to fetid and he noticed Christ's skin was now fur. It wasn't Jesus' body at all. He had his arm inside the dead buck. He pulled it out and found himself awake, breathing heavy in the cold air. The sun was not far below the horizon, giving off a deep blue light. In front of the car, a medium-sized black bear and two cubs gnawed on the carcass of the buck. Shug was asleep. Cigarette butts and the crumpled package lay scattered by his feet.

Thomas held his hands up to see if they'd actually been inside the buck. He gasped once he saw them covered in blood. But it was his own blood. The stubborn cut on his forehead had reopened, and stared at him from the rear view mirror like a third eye. He fell back to sleep.

❖❖❖

Thomas and Shug woke up to flashing lights behind them. Thomas walked to the police cruiser. The officer talked on his radio and drank coffee from a Styrofoam cup.

"You ought to clean all that crusted blood off your face before your father arrives," the policeman suggested.

"My father?"

"I called him. He's your ride home."

A man with a red bulbous nose stopped his pickup truck in front of Thomas's car and loaded the mangled, gnawed-on carcass into his truck bed. He shook hands with the police officer then drove off.

Thomas's father arrived with a carload of other kids. He was concerned about whether or not Thomas and Shug had head injuries and administered a series of unorthodox tests for concussions. "How long has your head been bleeding?" he asked his son.

"I don't know."

"It been bleeding since I started driving," said Shug.

"You let him drive?"

"Yeah," Shug said. "And he let me smoke his Marlboros so I wouldn't be scared of no bears."

Thomas's father looked down at the gravel. "Shug's friends were worried about him. I was worried about you both. We prayed all night. It was the only thing we could do. You hit a deer. Maybe that stopped you from a worse fate."

"Yeah maybe, like seeing an angel," Thomas said sardonically.

As they pulled away from the wrecked car in silence, Thomas saw a dirt road and by it an arrow-shaped sign. He remembered the donut man's instructions to turn right, here at this sign. But they passed it now. In a few minutes, they approached the Point-of-Rocks Bridge, and Thomas realized that they were not far from home. Michael's hill, as the man had called it, was really the palisades, right across the river from Thomas's house. He could sit on his back porch and see the angels.

"You could have crashed into anything on this damn road. Do you know that?" Thomas's father shouted. "That's how you die, you know. You die living. Do you know that?"

Something inside his father snapped. He let go the wheel, then laid into Thomas's face with four sloppy punches. The car miraculously followed the bend in the road. It was the first time that Thomas had ever been hit by his father, and the punches felt like nothing at all, not after so many months of Slinker's blows. His father pulled the car over on the shoulder with one hand, and seized his son's collar with the other. He clamped Thomas's neck with blood-smeared, shaking hands.

Choked of air, Thomas tried to pry his father's fingers off his neck, but he couldn't. Surging with rage, Thomas shifted his weight and launched an uppercut. His father's jaw broke with a snap. He threw a jab to the nose for good measure. Shug screeched like an owl in the back seat. The other kids didn't make a sound. His father let go and felt his jaw line with a creeping smile. Thomas gasped in a large breath. His lightheadedness went away as circulation returned and pushed a trickling of blood out his forehead.

His father squeezed his nostrils and breathed heavily. The two stared into each other's eyes, halfway recognizing who they were.

Alice Jay/Sweater Girl

When I was little, she was big. I cut her out and pinned her to the wall.
In the dark she jumped off the screen without a hair out of place.

Blonde, bad and beautiful. Dark men on white horses sniffed us out.
One threatened her life. Another—my face. Bloody and wet,

we trembled and moaned. A *femme fatale* lived to love. She taught me
how to wear a sweater. Cashmere and diamonds are soft and hard,

like the best of men. Between us we married ten.
Her daughter saved her life—or so the story goes.

A legend never touches a kitchen knife.
Once my son wanted to be a chef. His father lacked passion

for food and wine. He had an eye for young actors.
I, too, discovered a few. At fifteen she skipped typing

to buy a Coke. I will be discovered if I learn how to make love
to the camera. My smile is as tight as her sweater.

Alice Jay/The Silver Screen

Eleanor Parker, Eleanor Powell, Eleanor Rigby.
A song, a dance, a glance. That's entertainment.

A film, a poem, a play. I pray. I write
one poem, then another. Twelve, like the tribes.

Afternoons in the garden—without Allah—
my phone is off, my feet are up.

Fitzgerald leaned over a desk
on the lot. Coke bottles rimmed the room.

The scripts were doomed. Why hire a sculptor
when you need a plumber? The studio chose

my gowns and my guys. In another life
I was a star on the silver screen. I was told

I looked best in green. Now I wear white.
I refuse to fade into the garden. On the chaise

is a long, hard pad. The pen is from the Beverly Hills.
Too bad all the stars are on Hollywood Boulevard.

Tap, tap, tap. Words flow, or they don't.
Intervention isn't always divine. There was no rehab

then. You dried out in the desert. Or you were buried
along with your name, and everybody came.

R.T. Castleberry/Coupled

There is a Sunday wistfulness to late summer sunlight,
the rising rustle of a breeze.
I don't often see it.
I'm folded into my house early, after work.
Dulled by ceaseless disaffection,
I've become an instrument of routine, of resignation—
wrists bound by PC and cell phone,
constrained by family rant, familiar rage.
There is an order to this,
a symmetry to images of outburst:
I ask you three questions for the day.
Your answers wither through the seasons.
Settled, in a cycle
I chase the cigars-and-martini circuit.
You change your music with the moon.
We know the risk, the rhythm of our relationship:
advantage as a pair,
unkindness as an art.

Linda Lancione Moyer/Moving the Pig

My ex has been given a White House appointment.
He calls me from the Rotunda, where he's been
waiting for me in the crowd. I'm sweatily
washing dishes in the soup kitchen,
happy not to think of my real work,
but now I have to go home to my study
and move the pig.
Sprawled across my desk, black and fat,
he barely lifts his head when I come in.
I scratch his soft jowl,
coax him to my lap, then
slip him to the floor in the Unterlich
Maneuver, so often used in pig transport.
This is the nature of pig moving—
the pig's too heavy to lift outright,
and when you do hoist him up somehow,
he winds up a long way
from your notion of where he belongs.
The ex, still in touch by cell,
says the ceremony's started,
after which, he'll have two weeks in Mozambique,
and I'm still doing *what*?
The pig looks doleful,
hind end raised, front feet splayed.
His gold eyes ask just how much more of this
he must endure. He doesn't get
the eternal nature of what we're doing,
yet somehow pities me and wants to help.
Pressing the phone to my ear, I hear
raucous applause—next they're headed
to the rooftop restaurant. Once again
I tell him I can't. Now the pig's

in the seat of my swivel chair,
game but scared. When something
distracts his attention,
I seize him around the middle
and give one more heave.

Gail Rudd Entrekin/Experiment

(Prairie voles, unlike 95 percent of mammals, form
long-lasting bonds with their furry mates.)
—*Science News 10-15-08*

So researchers use them to study grief.
They take away one from the pair, isolate it,
and sure enough it mopes, stops eating,
stops reading the paper,
won't go out when they open the door.
Its personal hygiene suffers,
its little coat matted,
its little shoes repaired with duct tape.

Then they find out by slicing and dicing,
its brain is giving off corticotropin in massive doses,
its neurotransmitters flooded with the messengers
that deliver sorrow and loneliness. It wakes up
in the night howling; lab assistants tear at their own ears,
trying to stop the sound of its terrible pain.

The prairie voles dream of long tunnels under the dirt,
two black eyes shining at the far end, deep in a nest
of aloe and dung. They dream of running over the sand
side by side, and they question in their vast empty cages,
the wisdom of going on.
                              But now the researchers create
something else, a compound which blocks the sorrow signal.
Voila. No pain. *What mate?* the voles say.
Bring on the dancing girls in their little grass skirts
and mix me up a tequila sunrise. Some run laps
to keep in shape for a long and happy life,
do sit-ups, admiring the fancy clouds.
Others become Buddhist voles,
present in the moment.
All the prairie voles are happy
just to be alive.

Joanne Lowery/Coin

I will mint you myself:
Augustus of my prime
haloed with laurel,
pigtailed and presidential,
ubiquitous as Abe on copper.

Worth more than a cent
or Sacajawea's dollar,
exceeding farthing, pfennig and forint
in love's purchase,
gold nestled in my palm

you with your milled edges
impossible to counterfeit
will forever be my token.
Proud profile cast in relief
and minted from memory,

you weigh my heart with jingle.
I fish for the right amount:
you, a dime, one buffalo nickel.

Joanne Lowery/Arabesque

A ballet dancer always steps forward
with her right foot. It is grounded
first in wax, then bronze. Degas
knows both, how she stands tethered
to earth, a manmade stork. Or dances,
and this is just her first step.
Soon he will take his last,
reaching for her waist. Ah,
her slenderness is willing,
her left foot uplifted as she bends
to inspect the ground, arms outstretched
in a choreography of copper and tin.

James Doyle/Archaeological Proof

Great Gods bellow
out of the sun, wagon trains
plow up the Red Sea
well before noon, granaries
lap the late afternoon spills.

Adam and Eve
at dawn, Christ at three o'clock,
the rest of history
in between, Babylonian warlords
docking their armies at night.

It's true the burning
bush had the biggest voice,
but Moses spent
most of his time reading
the fine print

by direct sunlight. When
the fatted calf was finally
wheeled in, the moon
was rising
and Moses went berserk.

The long plain, the mountains,
the striders all disappear
at night for the smallest
itch. Only what's at hand
seems important.

Then the waking. Light
that has never occurred before.
The pages of the Bible
turning by themselves across
any desert you can name.

Anny Edinchikyan/One Dance

You flex, your muscles bulge—I need
to slide my hands against your flesh, like steel.
You look at me. Your eyes are hot with greed.
The music fills our souls, we dance, we feel.
Hours pass, then months. The seasons change—it's cold.
Your eyes turn gray, unclear; your touch is not
the same. You talk, but noise is all I hold.
The fault is mine. No, yours! As one we're caught.
I march alone, the streets my sole consort.
Each step takes me away—I trust myself.
This path I chose will help, I hope, to sort
my thoughts. I'm stuck—my legs are heavy, shelves.
At home I close my eyes and feel your skin
but hear your voice no more, you're gone; I grin.

Johanna Stoberock/The Strange Case of Ingrid P.

I lived with my husband at the edge of Manhattan. At night in the winter when the trees were bare we looked toward the Hudson River. We cherished our view, and waited all year for the cold when the leaves that hid the river would turn and swirl to the ground, the water revealing itself like a mountain behind mist: gray, silent in the distance. We lay in bed together in the morning and stared at the low clouds gathered in the sky and at the dull slate line beyond the hill and waited for the room to fill with more than just the flimsy specter that passed for light.

As we lay there, silent, side by side, I wondered if he led multiple lives as well. Instead of coming back from the store in the morning in the same state of completion in which he left, did part of him stay and stock shelves and speak Spanish and give back incorrect change? Did part of him leap into the newspaper's stories, across the ocean to Europe, to work to broker peace? Or was he somehow able to contain himself wholly within himself? Was he able to come back to me complete, and feel no longing strong enough to pull him away when he stared with me out the window at the river?

One day as I walked toward the cathedral on the wide avenue along which I lived, I looked to my right and saw the sun setting pink over the water. The bare, silhouetted trees formed a web, and the pink light was almost obscene in its intensity. I thought, *Right now, right now is one of my other lives. In this life I turn off my path and just keep staring at the icy river until the sun is gone from the sky. In this life, a man will approach me, and my dress will be long and a shawl will cover my shoulders instead of this bulky coat. The city behind us will be strangely silent, cars and electricity not yet invented, and the man will say. . . .* But a bird cooed, a car's brakes shrieked, and I found myself again in my regular winter coat, tapping my way across the cracks that striped the sidewalk.

❖❖❖

In one life I left my husband for the handsome young man at the post office, the one who at that time stood in line behind me every other Tuesday and who had recently begun to make idle conversation as we each waited for a window to become free. "You look tired today," he said. I blushed and looked down, flustered to have someone notice the shadows on my face. "It's going to be a long week," he said and, "All these letters—doesn't it overwhelm you to think about so much communication around us, so much communication, and all of it silent?" I smiled and agreed, and when we each nodded goodbye and stepped up to our separate counters, I realized that we could leave together if we chose. Another shape for my life to take. And as I watched, another Ingrid peeled off and left, arm in arm with the young man, laughing.

❖❖❖

My aunt came to visit one afternoon in another life. She brought a box of cookies. I made tea, and we sat together in the living room—this was the life in which my living room was filled with overstuffed furniture, and the lace curtains at the windows fluttered constantly, my life as the single woman I have always wondered whether I would be. My aunt put three spoonfuls of sugar in her tea, and then bit into a cookie. Her white hair was pulled back in a braid, the braid knotted intricately upon her head. The cookies were covered with powdered sugar. When she pulled the pastry away from her lips, the red was covered in white. I tried not to look at her as I stirred my own tea, and when I ate a cookie I made sure to place it directly between my teeth, my lips pulled archly back. The sweetness of everything was overwhelming.

"Have you met anyone?" she asked me, and I could see that her tongue was coated with sugar as well. "Have you met anyone you like?"

"I'm not really looking," I said. I couldn't tell her about Daniel, who had left the apartment, his shoes still untied, minutes before she arrived. "I'll let you know when something happens, I promise."

"Just so you're not shutting yourself in. Just so I know you're getting out from time to time."

"I go out."

"Of course you do."

"I do."

"Have another cookie, Ingrid. You look too thin."

It was always that way with my aunt. I couldn't tell her about my adventures, and she couldn't believe that I was the type of girl who would have adventures. I thought about Daniel as I took another sip of tea, about how I'd placed my hand on his shoulder and turned it like a knob so he faced me in bed this morning, and how his face, blurry as it moved in close to mine, would be echoing in my mind all day, maybe all week, and I nearly choked when the tea went down my throat too quickly.

"You be careful," my aunt said. "A single girl. You watch out."

When she left, I took another shower in my bathroom where all the towels matched—a perfect, rich cream color against the light blue walls—and where all the soap smelled of flowers. My single girl's apartment. Mine. I thought about Daniel in the shower earlier in the morning, and about how there's no way to share a shower without one person getting cold, and about how I'd washed his hair and he had washed mine. I loved living alone. I loved the hot water rushing on my shoulders, and dreaming.

There were several types of lives I knew I could lead. There was the life in which my husband died, and I spent five years grieving, but secretly couldn't understand my inability to feel a thing. In this life, after he died, it was as though I distanced myself from my body and anything connected with feeling, as though I was able to float five inches away from anything that caused a reaction. My husband had passed away, and I was alone, and the apartment filled with his absence. Then there was the life in which I was forty-five, not thirty-two, and I still had my figure, and thought nothing of sleeping with younger men. And the life in which I owned a cat. . .

As I walked that day along the avenue away from my apartment with the river at my right and the sun fading soft, the street was silent except for a flock of pigeons haplessly cooing from the top of a wall. Ahead of me, an elderly woman reached down and took a girl's tiny brown hand. The little girl was wearing a bright yellow parka. *Hot,* I thought, *in that coat. Hot,* and then I walked on, alarmed by the inarticulateness of my thoughts. A car swerved around the corner, a horn blared, and then the street lapsed into silence. *In this life,* I thought, *in this life I live in a quiet world interrupted only occasionally by the cooing of doves and the blaring of horns. In this life my thoughts are not fascinating. In this life I have left behind a dirty apartment and am heading towards the bank machine where my balance is dismally low. Which life is this? Does this life belong to me? This is not the life that I would choose, given a choice among the many lives of mine that I am certain exist. Give me my aunt. Give me the post office. Give me my husband in bed in the endlessly early morning when the river is still flat and gray and the trees are still naked.* This was my life of despair. The street remained quiet as I walked.

If nothing else, this life seemed consistent. I told myself it couldn't be a life in which I spent much time.

But the sky, even in this humdrum life, was beautiful, the pinks so bright they hurt my eyes, still caught in the gauze of the trees. The woman and child disappeared into a church. A car slowed down beside me, and, though I tried to look straight ahead and ignore it, the sound of someone whispering soon reached me. "Hey baby, hey baby, hey baby," came hissing over the curb and into my ears. "Hey baby, climb in with me, come and take a ride." It was all I could do not to look, but I balled my hands into fists and kept my eyes focused straight ahead.

The young man from the post office was a dancer. He invited me to a performance, and I was certain that the audience was padded with other women who had met him in circumstances similar to my own. I looked back and forth through the audience before the performance started to see if I could spot other women who wished to go home with him afterwards. There were too many for me to count.

When the house lights dimmed and the purple stage lights rose, I shivered. His costume, just a sleeveless T-shirt and loose pants, showed how strong his arms were. The loose fabric of the pants clung to his legs. I felt as though I was watching for things I shouldn't be. He picked up another dancer and held her on his hip with one arm wrapped around her waist. Would he be able to do that with me? Would I feel as light to him as she did? She was a tiny thing. Were they in love? I clapped with the rest of the audience when the piece was over. I knew his arms would stay in my mind forever.

Afterwards, we went out for a drink. "Did you like it?" he asked. "Did you love it?"

"I loved it," I answered.

"Even the part where I turn away?"

"Even that part. I loved it all."

We talked about what there was to love and the possibility of loving everything until the ice in our glasses melted, and our drinks were warm.

Occasionally my husband made me breakfast. Sausages fried in a cast iron pan. Orange juice in a wine glass. The window shades pulled up high.

Occasionally my husband and I curled up on the couch his parents had given us and read *The Sunday Times*. Occasionally the children playing in the park that separated our apartment from the river yelled and laughed like angels. Occasionally I fell asleep at night with my head in his lap, his fingers playing around my ear.

❖❖❖

Along with my life as a single girl, my life as a widow, my life with a cat, my life of despair, and my life with the handsome young man from the post office who invited me to his dance recitals, I had another life, and was not at all certain where it fit in. In it I took my elderly neighbor's dog for a walk in the park one afternoon. I've always hated dogs. I thought my neighbor was dying. He stopped me in the laundry room one day, and it took him five minutes to ask me the favor because he was doubled over with coughing. I could not say no when he asked. "Ingrid," he said, his hand cupping my cheek. "Ingrid, that dog will watch out for you. He'll take care of you, don't worry." I nodded, but I thought I would get my husband to do the task for me. And then I paused—I was no longer sure if this was a life in which I had a husband.

That afternoon when I took Alexander for a walk, I could not help but shiver. He was a middle-aged Great Dane and I felt like a child beside him. Our feet made crunching noises as we walked in the park through the snow. I watched Alexander's swaying tail until I suddenly realized that we had lost all remnants of daylight. The wind moaned through the trees. The snow swirled in narrowing spirals around us. Alexander, as big as a giant, began to chase ghosts. He pulled me behind him, and we lunged through shadows, growled into the dark, tore around trees, almost touching the invisible world, but always just missing. I tugged at Alexander's leash, and even as he pulled me forward, I felt myself chased by the same ghosts that, scared by the dog's loud bark, had circled around to terrorize us from behind. I called to Alexander as loudly as I could through clenched teeth, tried to pull him in tightly, cursing my too thin arms, resisting the shiver creeping up my spine. He lunged forward and bolted, but we never caught a ghost that we could hold. When we finally got back to the building and I knocked on my neighbor's door, there was no answer. I had keys. I let us in. On the counter was a note saying he'd had to go to the hospital, could I feed Alexander? This is what my elderly neighbor was like—he thought of everything even as the ambulance waited.

The walls in his apartment were covered with paintings. I tiptoed through the rooms, waiting for my heart to still, quiet as a nail. His bed was made. His bathroom sink looked as though it had just been wiped clean. *What are his other lives?* I wondered. *Am I the only one who peels away? Am I the only one who's not complete?* There was a card on his refrigerator from a niece. "Uncle Roger," she called him, and signed it, "Love, Mary Anne." To me he was just Mr. Anderson. How could he live a life where he had a niece? Why wasn't Mary Anne here walking his dog? I thought of his hand on my cheek. How could he live a life without me?

I sat down on a couch and listened to Alexander lapping water. The paintings glowed as if lit from within. *If I lived here,* I thought, *I'd dream myself walking through painted forests and stroking painted faces. I'd listen to painted music and through my listening, it would come free from the flat surface to which it was condemned. If I lived here, my lives would be laid out before me; I would have them all in front of me to see at once.* When Alexander jumped onto the sofa beside me and licked my cheek, I shook my head. It was time to leave. The multiplicity of available lives can be dizzying. I needed my warm bed to wonder at the wealth.

As I walked toward the cathedral along the avenue, and felt a part of myself tear off to go to the park by the river, I trembled here, in this life, with the hope for what that part of me might find, and with the agony that it might find nothing, and with the question that even if it found happiness in that life, would I ever truly know about it in this? I whispered to myself, *You have a husband at home making dinner. You have a ticket to go to France next spring. You have a full year's subscription to* **The New York Times**—*this life is not so bad.* Just then a car drove by, stopping briefly at the light before skidding away. A woman sat in the back seat, her black hair knotted in a bun. *That is me,* I thought, *that is me and I just watched myself leave and part of me will never come back. How can I remain whole even when that part of me has left? How can I remain and not be whole?* The bells at the cathedral rang. The sun set beyond the river. My husband called me home.

Catherine Johnson/The One Thing I've Never Told Anyone

(A) Now I always look at the fingers of boys I find attractive
on the bus. Shape, width, length—cleanliness is key. I look at
fingers and imagine how they would feel between my
legs, how many would fit inside. Wonder the degree
of the skin's roughness. But if the fingernails are dirty,
despite his level of overall appeal, I stop there. Refuse
to close my eyes. Refuse to lie back in dark sheets (nighttime
fantasy formed in the sunlit heat of a bus) to feel his touch.
    But if I do, the imagined faces always blur into One.

(B) In the military, they train men in moonlit forests. Staying
off the path to avoid "capture," carrying seventy-two pounds
on backs, shadow branches slashing the soft faces
of our sons and husbands. All learn to slaughter and prepare
a rabbit at the same time, stars blinking in wind brushed
branches above. If you fail to crush the spine at the exact
place the rabbit will shriek—cry out like a child. He
described the black air, iced and weighing in on shoulders, as
the trees trembled with the screams. His was a lop-ear.
    Tried to end her quick and painless.

(C) I was twenty two and still never been kissed. We stood
on the side of a mountain, cliché dome of the celestial kind
spread overhead. He had very clean fingernails. Kept pressing
his nose against my cheek so I finally just asked if he was
trying to kiss me. He stepped away, embarrassed, said
Well not anymore and asked me not to tell anyone—
When we finally kissed his fingertips were rough
as they moved to find the spine behind my neck.

Suzanne Roberts/What the Dead Sometimes Do

Sometimes they are smoking
under the coral light of a desk lamp.

Sometimes they are drinking rye, ignoring the typewriter,
the nest of crumpled papers in the wastebasket.

Sometimes, they are looking through their files for an early draft
of something, but they can't remember what.

Sometimes, they are asking, "What about me?"
"What about my life?"

Sometimes they are too drunk to talk, their silence
the bridge between the voice and its echo.

Charles Rammelkamp/Nymphomaniac

"Impotent Jake Barnes is hopelessly in love
with nymphomaniac Lady Brett,"
the student in my English 201 class wrote
in his final exam essay,

and I realized I hadn't seen that word
in print in decades, a term tossed
onto the junk heap of linguistic history,
since the women's movement fingered it sexist.

The archaic word conjured Elizabethan insults.
A whitely wanton with a velvet brow.
Cock'red silken wanton.
Dissembling harlot, deceitful dam.

Doesn't it simply mean a woman
who enjoys sex the way a man does?
But I remembered its impact
when I was a high school kid.

The Science teacher was whispered to be
crazy for anything with a cock,
unable to control her desires,
reckless as a drunk, satisfying them.

And of course I recalled
the stories of girls impaled on gearshifts
in drive-in movies, unable to contain
themselves in their boyfriends' absence.

But I felt wistful for its loss,
as I might mourn the death of a pet,
for the images the word summoned,
the promises it seemed to make.

Ruth Thompson/Translations

What word does it make, that calligraphy
of half-turned head and spine?
You stand in such privacy of bone
there in the doorway,
looking back at me:

Sister.
Your body speaks to me,
our Yoknapatawpha.
I too drift in its tides, sea-warm
as blood and thick with worlds.

Ah, we were cried forth in a black night!
as lightning speaks from the sky's cracked skull
to name some territory, and yet

no word can tell me what I want to know,
not even this one:
heron-legged in the sun,
looking back at me
between one thing and another.

Ruth Thompson/Bless You, Father Walt

for lying stripped and singing
in the floes and fallows of your own body

for granting us land-rights
to your shaggy unkempt tongue

where through long syllables of scarlet leaves
we ride shanks-mare, drunk on the public road again.

Oh, bless me, Father Walt—
lend me your large boots to caper and hoot at dusk

make me shameless and grandiose,
tender and foolish and brave.

Bless this false coin I use, stained as tinker's ware,
turn it to tigers resting in the arches of my mouth.

Nick Conrad/Thunder

After Jim Dine

Sans fingers, hands, wrists,
sans those slender arms,
sans that sweet caress,
sans those gentle hands
held just so. Sans head,
sans its imagined
pose at the end
of her slender neck,
sans that knowing nod.

Relic and yet not,
with a songbird perched
atop her throat.

Sans lips, ears, eyes. . .
Sans hair long or short,
straight or curled, loose
or coifed, brown, blonde,
red, or raven black.

At night, a wolf
sleeps at her feet.

Her torso is turned,
as if she has just
shifted to look
your way. Her legs,
trapped in the plinth,
root her chaliced hips.
Her gaze, lightning,
and after, thunder.

Azatuhi Babayan/Albatross

In a virtually empty room, he examines
The multicolored capsules neatly lined up.

Three a.m., melting into another week—in grave,
Deafening silence on this bed made
Of dead leaves and (things)
Too hard to shake off and finally rest.
In sweeps a breath of weightlessness,
And a rush of life flees from the cage
That houses everything;
All of a sudden,
Nothing.

Awake—
He stares into the distance
At dissolving colors with clouded vision
On the very edge of a cliff where he
Once learned how to fly and stay
Aloft when the tide began to rise.
Up from below and picked to the bone,
Slight misunderstandings and unspoken words
Slowly float to the surface, linger.

A body breaks the calm in one swift motion;
Its hollow hull sinks to the bottom.

Joshua Ruffin/The Way My Uncle Smoked

Stan held his like an assassin
would a knife, thumb
and two fingers, concealed
on the underside of his wrist,
ready to flick it at a killer.
He could do it, too—300 lbs
easy, but nimble as a wren
from the shoulders out,
I once saw him snatch
a cicada from the air
with his free hand and slap
it against the barn door,
all in a blink while telling
my mother how to keep
the sumbitch aphids
off her watermelons.

Most things he did were fast,
sinister. Thanksgiving morning
he'd gut a deer for sausage
and, after splitting the belly
in a single stroke, would have
the carcass skinned and the good meat
harvested before my cousins
were finished dumping
the organs into the oil drum
burning behind the shed.

With his smoking, though, he was slow
and gentle. After a last drag
he'd let the ember hang in his loose fist,
letting the smoke gather itself
into a mass of tendrils
before dropping the butt

to the red earth and showing
his palm, as if releasing
the last two doves on Earth.

Susan R. Williamson/Driving Back from the Antique Shop

I strap Buddha in beside me with a seatbelt.
He rides shotgun, in eternal meditation—
motionless, made of jade—a divine light
suspended above his head, topped
with a fringed shade.

Whoever painted his peaceful smile,
closed lids, couldn't understand dangers
nowadays. Probably never conceived
of Buddha zipping down Main Street
with a woman at the wheel.

I too left my father's house, every event
some mystic signifier, as I read the Greeks,
met the French. "Do you know, Buddha,"
I ask, looking over, moving fast. . . "how
afraid I can be?"

Even, bare breasted, high-heeled, silk shirt,
cropped hair, weekends spent recycling,
all the while—the alms bowl goes empty.
How my heart is begging. You see me,
don'tcha Buddha?

Sure, I get by, another myth I swallow
whole, chase with pills, potions, stress
tests. Yes, and long massages. I'll come
with you—or I'll take you with me—
as an amulet, safe, strapped in.

I'll pull over somewhere, under a Bodhi tree,
and then you tell me, you open those eyes,
fix them straight ahead, tell me what
it means to fly. To pull over to the side,
get off this road. Ascend.

Brian Keenan/Something from Nothing

The dermatologist's clinic was in a strip mall. Despite being sand-wiched between a Kinko's and an Armed Forces Recruiting Station, it was pretty much like a doctor's office anywhere, with insurance forms to fill out, a few potted plants that may or may not have been fake, and Muzak versions of Phil Collins and Sting piped into a lobby cluttered with vinyl furniture and badly out of date copies of *Ladies' Home Journal*. The reception counter had a candy dish filled with those colored conversation hearts labeled with familiar, bizarre phrases: "HOT STUFF," "SAY YES," and "BE MINE." It was Valentine's Day. Outside it had been cold and snowy for months, with no sign of a let-up, my car was breaking down, my ex wouldn't return my phone calls, and I had a spot on my tongue. The spot was white, about the size of a dime, pale and neatly ovular. A discoloration, I'd come to call it, having no better idea of what it was or what it portended.

The dermatologist was a tall man who wore scrubs and squinted over his glasses. He scratched his stubble while flipping through a book of skin conditions. He let me look, too. "Here," he said, pointing at a picture of one. The picture was of a person's entire mouth, and little milky spots, connected by spidery white lines, lined the cheeks. A spot resided on the tongue. The spot wasn't anywhere near as neatly ovular as mine.

The dentist had actually noticed it first. I'd been in there about a month before, getting my teeth cleaned. I'm big on clean teeth. People give other people extra points for nice teeth, whether they realize it or not. We're big on smooth skin, big handshakes, and pearly white smiles. So I try to keep up. The dentist had been baffled, to say the least. "I've never seen anything like this, Henry," he'd said. His chair-side manner had a bit of an alarmist streak, apparently—not real comforting. "It's some kind of discoloration. Go to an oral surgeon. They may want to do a biopsy." I knew what the word biopsy meant. Watch enough hospital shows on TV and you pick up some things.

The oral surgeon, though, hadn't wanted to do a biopsy. Said it didn't look like cancer; it didn't look "irregular" enough. Too "neatly ovular." I was almost proud of my regular, ovular spot, then. He didn't know what it was, though. Maybe he was too busy thinking about its neat ovular-ity, resenting that such graceful symmetry didn't give him license to cut.

Surgeons like cutting, something you pick up on around season one of *E.R.* It's part of their character. "Keep an eye on it," he'd said. I could see him mentally packing away his scalpel, gazing wistfully at his suture line. "Go to a dermatologist if you notice any changes."

I hadn't noticed any changes, but not having a name for my spot bothered me. It wasn't cancer; okay, then what was it? The dermatologist had sighed. He'd had me stick out my tongue, then poked it, prodded it, and pulled it, taken a break to scratch his chin and clean his glasses with the tail of his scrub shirt, done a little bit more poking and prodding, then folded his arms across his chest. "You have a white discoloration," he said, "about the size of a dime." Tell me something I don't know, I thought.

So he produced the book. I took a long, hard gander at the picture of the white spot. I had to admit it was better than the picture next to it, of a mouth riddled with white sores, some leaking pus. "It could be that one, too," he said, and I wasn't so reassured, anymore. The second one—the sores and pus—was precancerous. Biopsy, I thought. That's a word that stays on a person's mind. I'd mentioned the prospect to Anne, my ex, when we were still together, things having fallen apart more or less recently. She'd made me stick my tongue out, handled it, touched the spot. "You don't have cancer," she'd said. How the hell could she know? "Don't be so dramatic," she'd said. That she was a community theater producer with no medical training whatsoever didn't trouble her. Anne liked to pin things down. This was this and that was that. Things were or they weren't. In that respect we had something of a personality clash.

The first possibility, the one that wasn't precancerous, was probably less serious. Then again, worst-case scenario, it could be Hepatitis C. Or HIV. Pick your poison. Most likely, the dermatologist assured me as he snapped the book shut, it was nothing. Keep an eye on it. He and the oral surgeon must have gone to the same school. Probably nothing. He used a big fancy term that I immediately forgot.

"Come again?" I said.

"It's kind of like something from nothing." He gave his cheek a good, swift scratch. For a dermatologist, I started to wonder if he might not have something going on with all that scratching.

"Sure," I said, "something from nothing. Of course."

He wrote me a prescription for a paste I was to apply to the spot every night before bed. I could get it at any pharmacy, better sooner than later. Suddenly needing a drink very badly, I opted for later.

My car started, no longer a guarantee by any means, but the heat was as dead as ever. It'd kicked the bucket around Christmas, victimized by the heater core, the blower motor, the fan, or some other problem I didn't know the name of. I had vague plans to fix it, buy a repair manual and do it myself, but those hadn't yet come to pass, and probably what I was really hoping for was to just get through the rest of the winter. It took a lot of scraping, as the defrost didn't work, either. I scraped the outside windows while I waited for the engine to warm up. I scraped the inside while I was waiting some more. Driving along, my breath would freeze up on the windows, so I scraped at intersections—stop signs, red lights. Almost two months went by like that, scraping. It had driven Anne near crazy. She'd work on her side of the car with a little scraper from the real estate office that clipped to the flip-down visor, usually getting less than sparkling results—two little lines from the edges of the scraper everywhere. "We're going to freeze to death in here," she'd say. I'd agree it was possible, trying to ignore it, finding the little clear places in the windshield to look through. "I feel trapped in here," she'd say, leaning forward awkwardly in her seat, trying to find the right angle to scrape. That, too, I could ignore. "We can't go on like this," she'd say, her elbow almost clocking me in the face. Reluctantly, I'd agree. "I need some space," she'd finally said one day. What good response has anyone ever had to that?

On the way home from the clinic, peering through the clear spot I'd scraped on the windshield, I tried to call Anne. Her phone rang and rang. Maybe she was at the theater, booking shows and actors, drawing up flyers, taking a long lunch, whatever exactly a community theater producer does all day. I was never really sure on the details, though we'd been together almost six months. Then she'd moved across town to live with one of her friends, a forty-something guy with a pot belly and a bad haircut, an actor in one of the plays she produced. That's when she came out with the space thing. She denied there being anything *untoward*—her word—going on with the actor, but the timing was suspect. Suspect, to say the least.

The snow was piled high against the concrete median, flecked with black and brown from the wintertime exhaust. My speakers didn't work too well, either. Just a small glimmer of sound—the tinny shadow of a singer's voice—issued from the driver's side door, against occasional electronic rasps and coughs from the speaker. The car—a '92 Ford Tempo—had cost me all of 800 bucks, so maybe I didn't have a right to ask for too much. Still, it seemed like a sign of the times. I half-expected the engine to fall out onto the roadway, the way things were going, or to get pulled over on principle for driving such a heap.

And here's the thing: Technically speaking, I shouldn't have been driving at all, on account of a bad choice made a couple months previous. The state was holding onto my license for a little while. I could see their point, actually, and I was risking somewhere north of twenty days in jail, but still, a guy had to make a living, and, after all, I had a spot on my tongue. A discoloration.

Anne's phone went to voicemail.

"Just calling to see how you're doing," I said, above the rattle of car on the road, the speaker's garble. "Call me back."

The sun was going down over the hills around town when I got home. After hanging up my coat and throwing my hat and gloves on the couch, I stuck out my tongue and checked out my spot in the bathroom mirror. It looked the same as ever. "Don't look at it for a week," the dermatologist had said as he hustled me to the receptionist and my bill, "that way you'll be able to notice any changes." I don't know how I was supposed to put on the paste without looking at the spot. Good plan, Doc, I thought. You try it. I grabbed a beer from the fridge.

My apartment looked out over a big lake that was frozen over with a thick layer of snow. It was only a one-bedroom apartment but it had a sliding glass door that led out onto a balcony. In the late fall, when Anne and I had still been going good, we'd sit out on the balcony in these camping chairs I had, and we'd drink gin and tonics until Anne's cheeks flushed red with the chilly wind off the lake. The chairs were buried now under a foot of snow, their color faded by the sun and wind and cold. The snow had piled up by the door, too. When I'd had a couple beers, watching TV, listening to the steady hum of the refrigerator, waiting for Anne to call back, I opened up the door. I had half a mind to sit outside and have a cocktail, for old time's sake. Snow tumbled down into the room. I tried to sweep it off the carpet, back outside. My hands went numb with cold and the carpet got wet with the melting snow. I shut the door again.

Over the winter I'd taken up cross-country skiing. Since I'd had my job—I sat at a computer most of the day, made enough money for an okay apartment and a lousy car—I'd gotten a little thick around the middle, and it felt good to be out in the open air, working my legs, working my shoulders and chest muscles with each plant and pull with the poles. I'd do a lap or two around the lake in the morning. Sometimes Anne went with me. She didn't like it too much. There were no ready-made trails on the lake to follow, and the going was made slower by the chaotically crisscrossing tracks of snowmobiles, so it was hard to pick up any rhythm of kick, glide, kick, glide. She preferred the groomed trails at the university, and complained just enough that I stopped asking her to come, after a while.

The moon was coming up over the lake. From far away, in my apartment, you couldn't see the snowmobile and ski tracks. From up close it looked like the choppy surf of the ocean, or Lake Michigan, which I'd seen once, but from my apartment it was flat and calm and undisturbed, the furrows evened out by distance and the moonlight. The trees on the far side of the lake were still visible. I lived on the edge of town, and past the lake the woods were dense; you could walk for miles, encountering only overgrown, rutted dirt roads for hunting access, infrequently-used snowmobile and ATV trails, or the occasional power line stretching off to who-knows-where. An easy piece of dirt to get lost in. You want *space*? I thought. Here's space for you. Nothing but. I finished my beer, put the rest in a backpack, bundled back up in my coat and hat and gloves, and dug my skis out of the corner behind the door.

I had an ice fishing spot on the far side of the lake. A couple Saturdays a month I'd rent a diesel-powered ice auger and drill down through the ice, spend the day drinking cheap beer, pulling out undersized fish that I'd throw back. I'd thought about building a little hut, but it never happened. Instead I'd sit out there on overturned five-gallon buckets, sometimes with a buddy from work, throw a line in the water, and sip beer. When the ice was thick enough I'd build a fire out of scrap lumber, hauled out there a little at a time. One time Anne came out with me. She wouldn't let me build a fire, convinced the ice would melt. No amount of explaining about the thickness of the ice or the way such a fire works would sway her. A stubborn girl, that Anne, even dead wrong. It was admirable, maybe endearing.

There was still a little wood left. I imagined Anne cooking dinner with her actor roommate, cuddling on the couch with him, watching a movie. I didn't know for sure they were sleeping together, but I had a feeling. Like I said, it was suspect. I kept matches, lighter fluid, and some newspaper under one of the buckets. The wood took a while in catching. I drank steadily but couldn't taste a thing. It might have been the spot. The universe had clearly taken a turn against me.

Maybe I have to get used to this, I thought, not wholly sure what *this* referred to. Accept it. Maybe it's a part of growing up.

Clouds had settled in overhead; the moon was close and surrounded by a halo of white. Snow. More snow. The time Anne came out here we'd caught fish and kept a couple of them. She'd taken a shot at pulling her own out of the water. At first she didn't like it. "How do I get them off the hook?" she'd asked, afraid of the fish wriggling in her hands, trying desperately, unthinkingly, to get back to the icy hole from which she'd yanked it. She'd petted the fish. "They're not icky at all," she'd said, as if I'd accused them of that. She'd placed it in my little Styrofoam cooler, taking care to hold it while the life pulsed out of it, then raking the cubes of ice over it, like dirt on top of a makeshift grave. When I fried them up later on the balcony, she didn't eat a single bite. I love this girl, I'd thought.

That's not to say it was a surprise, us coming apart, her with the actor friend, and whatever was going on there. It wasn't. "You take things too seriously," she'd say. Or, "you don't take things seriously enough." Whichever way, I knew she was right. Fires on the ice, no, spots on your tongue, maybe, but she tended to be dead-on about that kind of thing.

The fire finally caught. I kept it small. I wasn't much in the mood for it, anyway. I put the empty beer can under the other bucket, opened another one. For a long time I stood out there, drinking slowly, watching the fire and the collection of clouds overhead, feeling safely tucked away from the lights and terraces of the lake front buildings, including my own.

She didn't eat a single bite of the fish. Had I found that endearing? The wind lightly swirling, the fire crackling, it struck me as stubborn, childish, self-important. That went for needing space, too, and whatever she was doing with the actor. Eat some of the goddamn fish. There are plenty of them. I found the hole I'd bored out the previous weekend. Ice had formed over the top of it, solid enough to resist the initial strikes with my hand. I pulled a section of scrap two-by-four from the pile and drove it down against the ice. My first effort thudded off defiantly, but a thick white splotch, something like a bruise, formed where I'd connected. On the next blows the top layer of ice splintered, small sections gave way, and then I was through.

For a moment I just looked at the hole, the floating chunks of ice, the bored-out sides, the black water that I couldn't see through. Behind the woodpile I kept a little kid's fishing rod that a buddy had brought out. The reel was broken. I found a can of corn under the bucket and warmed it over the fire until the ice loosened and I could get out the kernels. "Dinner's ready," I said to the fish. "Come and get it."

I lowered the line down into the hole and waited. Away from the immediate range of the fire, the night was cold. I wished I had someone to talk to. I worked my tongue around my mouth, touching the roof, the lips, the gums under the bottom teeth. Maybe the spot would freeze off if I stood out here long enough.

I grew worried that my line wasn't far down enough. It was hard to see. Chunks from the ice I'd broken up floated around the hole. I put the fishing rod down, and, on my knees, reached into the hole, searching for the ice. I pulled up chunk after chunk. My gloves got soaked with the cold water. I put them by the fire, happy to have the hole cleared. I balled up one fist and stuck it in my pocket, held the fishing rod from halfway inside the other pocket.

I finished the beer and took another one. The fish didn't seem to have any interest. When I'd crumpled the empty can of my next beer in my hand, I considered packing it up. I started to long for my warm couch and the glow of the TV. Then I felt a tug on the line. I waited, and when I felt the bite again, I jerked the line up, trying to hook the fish. I pulled the line in, hand over hand. The fish was long and shiny with ice water. Not long enough, no doubt, but it's not like Fish and Game or the cops were out there to check. I held him up and looked him over in the icy cloud of my breath.

Setting him aside, I went back to work. Soon I felt another tug on the line, and started to reel in the next fish. I held him up in my hands. His mouth gaped tiny bubble questions. "Don't ask me, buddy," I said. "I guess that's the way it goes. Ours is not to wonder why." Then I noticed the first fish. He was flopping dangerously close to the hole. I went down to my knee and tried to scoop him up with my free hand. As I did, the other fish wriggled free. I tried to pin it against my chest but lost my balance a little, and it jumped back into the hole. I reached in after it, too late, but in time to feel the first fish dive back into the hole, too. It was a damn jailbreak. The water level went up into the hole, though, so until the fish swam under the walls of the hole—which they could do easily enough—they swam around in the small circumference. I searched the water with both hands for the fish. I pinned one against the side and carefully pulled it out. When I got it back to the surface of the hole, I pitched it towards the woodpile and went back for the other fish. I splashed around for a while, but he must have slipped back down into the lake. "You're lucky this time, guy," I said, but really I was kind of proud of him. He'd beaten some long odds, getting back into that lake.

At first, my car wouldn't start, and I thought it might have finally quit for good, but the engine eventually creaked, rattled to life. I set to scraping the windshield, outside and in. The front of my jacket was wet with lake water, but the inside seemed fine, and my gloves had dried a little by the fire. The fish was tucked into the inside pocket of my coat, which bulged as I put on the seat belt. I tossed the backpack still filled with beer in the passenger seat, grabbing one for the ride.

Before I'd left the lake I'd done what might have been a dumb thing and called Anne again. She didn't pick up, as usual. I'd stuttered a little, unable to think of something to say. Then I'd remembered what I'd forgotten before. "Happy Valentine's Day," I said. Across the line, riding on waves bouncing off of satellites, the silence was deafening. I panicked. "The doctor says I might have cancer," I said, and quickly hung up. Anne lived on the other side of the town, about a ten mile drive. He had practically said that, I told myself. In so many words. It was in the ballpark of having been said, at the very least.

On the way to Anne's I stopped at the Wal-Mart pharmacy. Might as well, I figured. Only inside the store did I realize that I still had the fish in my pocket. I must have got some ice into the pocket, too, and it was melting fast, because my chest was suddenly very damp and very cold. I worried a little about the smell, too, as I stepped into the line. For the first but certainly not the last time that night, I wondered if I'd have been better off staying at home. A woman in a thick jacket, boots, and a frumpy hairdo turned around and gave me the once over. "Happy Valentine's Day," I said. She smiled thinly and turned back around. I tapped my foot on the floor, trying to kill the time before my turn.

The pharmacist, or maybe she was just a clerk, some kind of low-level pharmacist that would be working the night shift, had deep wrinkles around her mouth, and she wore too much eye makeup. She hardly looked up as she got the prescription and brought it back to the counter. "Apply a thin coating once daily," she read from the label on the box as she rang me up.

"Thank you," I said. She raised her eyebrows a little, still looking down at the register. I swiveled on my feet as if to leave, then stopped, turned back, and tapped the box on the counter. "How many times a day do I apply it?" I asked. Maybe I just wanted any reaction out of her at all, any expression besides no expression. It's not too hard to notice people, I wanted to tell her. We've all got problems. Some of us might have cancer. She finally looked up at me. She took a short breath, set her lips hard together. Other than that, nothing. Reaching over, she plucked the box from my hand, held it out about foot from her face.

"Once," she said. She handed the box back to me. "A thin coating." I nodded. Have it your way.

"Happy Valentine's Day," I said as I left, but she had already turned back to her computer screen, and if she heard me, it didn't show.

In the car I angled the rearview mirror to get a look at my spot. The tube of paste was smaller than I'd expected, like a travel tube of toothpaste. I squirted a little bit of the paste out onto my finger. It was thick and gummy, like a glop of clumpy Vaseline. My spot looked about the same as ever, maybe bigger. Still impressively ovular. I tried to rub the paste on it, but it wouldn't come off my finger. "Fuck," I said. I was starting to like the sound of my voice with no one around. I sucked the saliva into the back of my mouth, trying to dry my tongue out. With a little work, the paste came off my finger, though it was hard to tell if it was exactly on the spot. When I shut my mouth the paste stuck to the roof of my mouth. I worked it back onto the tip of my tongue, but then it scraped off on my front teeth. "Fuck," I said again, this time louder.

I rinsed my mouth out with a sip of beer and drove over to Anne's.

Anne must have gone out for Valentine's Day dinner with the actor, I figured, because his car was gone from her driveway. I'll just drop off the fish, I thought, as a token. That made sense to me, it really did. I parked my car and looked for something to put the fish in, coming up with a plastic bag from the back seat. I tied the bag tight and put the fish back in my coat pocket.

The first thick flakes of snow were falling when I got out of the car. They stuck to the windshield and melted on my scarf. The walk up to Anne's front porch had been shoveled, the snow piled neatly on either side. I pictured the actor bundled up in his coat and hat, sweating over his shovel in the early morning, and Anne watching him from the front door, a cup of tea in her hand. I've never rooted so hard for a snow-shoveling-induced heart attack.

Just then a light turned on over the porch. It lit up the snowy front yard, me included. The door opened. It took me a second to adjust my eyes to the light, but there was no mistaking Anne. She didn't have a cup of tea, though, she had a cordless phone.

"Henry?" she said. "What are you doing here?"

I couldn't answer at first. I'd been expecting her to look, well, worse. Bags under her eyes, like she hadn't been sleeping well. Hair messed up from anxiety. Over what? Missing me, I guess. Instead, she looked great. Fresh. Her skin glowed in the porch light. She wore a pair of faded blue jeans and a sweater which her small breasts filled out gamely. The curls of her hair—she'd usually straightened it when we were together—fell down across her shoulders. They were a revelation to me. I couldn't think of a thing to say to her. I was interrupting an occasion, a life that didn't include me, as if I'd knocked on the door of a stranger. And maybe I had.

"I tried calling," I said. She was a little too far away to use my normal voice, and I didn't want to yell, but I didn't feel encouraged to close the distance.

"I know," she said. She paused. I tried to look past her, for the actor. I didn't know what I'd say to him. Maybe he would threaten me, cause a scene, try to beat me up.

"You can't keep calling all the time," Anne said. "It's getting too much. I feel like you're stalking me. Porter thinks we should just call the police."

"Fuck Porter," I said under my breath.

"What?" Anne said.

I cringed. Restraint had escaped me again.

"I'm not stalking you," I said. I was trying not to yell. "I missed you."

I felt the fish in my pocket. I brought you this, I thought of saying. Then I realized the kind of gesture that would make. I didn't get you any chocolate or flowers, you're probably having a nice dinner with a guy who's not half-drunk and soaking wet, but here, have this once-living creature that you'll never eat. Anne crossed her arms, leaned against the doorjamb.

"I went to the doctor today," I told her.

"I heard something about that," she said. I think she was trying to smile, trying to make it nice between us. With a little wood going in the fireplace, a couple mugs of hot chocolate, a blanket shared between us, and old Porter clutching his chest on the sidewalk, she might have succeeded.

"You don't have cancer, do you?" she asked.

I looked down at the snow, pawed at the ground with my foot, still wearing my ski boots.

"I didn't think so," Anne said. She was very confident in her ability to read me. It probably wasn't totally unearned, and I had to admire her confidence, her arrogance. She had a way of making strengths out of her faults. "You've been to how many, two doctors already? Why don't you take their word for it?"

"Why don't you?" I said. It was not what I'd meant to say at all. I think I'd been going for something along the lines of "You try it"—not exactly an adequate, adult response, either. And I'd pretty definitely been yelling.

"What?" she asked. I didn't repeat it. She looked behind her, made a quick motion like telling a dog to stay, and stepped out onto the porch. She closed the door behind her.

I kept my mouth closed, as if she'd be able to see my spot—my discoloration—from so far away. I was ashamed of it, all of a sudden. Not of its grossness, because it wasn't particularly gross, just a white spot, but of the strange pride I realized I'd had in it. I felt like a grade school kid who wants glasses, just for the attention: look at *me*, there's something wrong with *me*.

"I just wanted to tell you," I said. "Happy Valentine's Day." That, at least, said calmly.

Anne nodded. I retreated a step or two. She frowned. Could she smell the fish? She must have seen the front of my jacket, still damp with water.

"Look," she said. She looked like she didn't know what to say next. I turned to go.

"Henry," she said. I turned back to her. Waited.

"I just—" she said. That same look of concern. "I just don't know what it is with you. You've got to get over it. You know, not just us, I mean. Everything."

She sighed, fiddled with the phone's antenna. She had small hands and she chewed her fingernails. I missed that very much. "I'm not trying to be mean. I'm really not. Just, you know, you don't have to be so *aggrieved*."

"Aggrieved," I said.

"Yes." She sighed, and smiled, like we'd been in a contest for a word to describe me and *aggrieved* took the prize. My condition had a name, and that was that. I nodded. I might have even smiled.

"Okay," I said. "All right."

Anne went back to the door and waited with her hand on the doorknob while I started the car. I left the door open and sat there for a second, half in the car and half out. The engine shuddered for a second, like an actress in a movie just before a faint, and I thought it was going to stall or give out, but it caught again. Okay, aggrieved. All right. Touché. But then I couldn't let it go. That couldn't end it. It wasn't fair to end it in one word. Or maybe it was, but it sure as hell wasn't fair that she got to pick the word.

I got out of the car, scraper in my hand. Anne stood in the doorway. "Listen," I said, most certainly yelling, but I couldn't think of anything else. I watched my breath. I clutched the scraper hard. Then Anne withdrew into the doorway. A man stood beside her; I could see his hand on Anne's shoulder. She was talking quietly but animatedly, like she was in an argument. The hand on her shoulder grabbed the phone still in her hands. She held it tight at first, still whisper-arguing, but he tugged at it, and she let go. She didn't look back, and the door closed. After a few moments the porch light went out.

The fish jabbed at my chest when I tried to sit down in the car. I sat there, the radio bleating its scratchy, barely-heard songs. Then I got back out of the car, and walked again up to Anne's porch, treading softly. Taking the fish out of my pocket, I looked around the house. I tossed the bag under the porch. As I did, the outside light flicked on, apparently not sensitive to ex-boyfriends trudging drunkenly around the front yard, but worth every penny when it came to them tossing a fish around. I scampered back to the car, scraped fast and furious, and backed out of the driveway in a hurry.

The streets were deserted. The parking lots of the strip malls and supermarkets were mostly empty. I don't know exactly where the cops came from. But suddenly, back near the Wal-Mart, there they were, behind me, blue and red lights flashing.

Over the next two months I'd do my best with the paste, try to sleep with it getting stuck to the roof of my mouth, teeth, and cheeks. I had plenty of time to figure it out, to keep an eye out for changes, to notice things getting irregular. I didn't notice anything, but when I was able to visit the dermatologist again in the spring, he couldn't detect the spot at all. "Idiopathic," he said, nodding his head, as if that still actually explained something.

And maybe it did. Things happen to people. There isn't always a good reason. You get stuck in towns you don't like, towns where it snows too much, where your car breaks down, where you never feel quite warm. And life goes on. But I didn't know that then. The state gave me ninety days to figure it out, sixty for my second DUI, twenty for driving on a suspended license, and another ten for who knows what. I got sent to a halfway house, where I scored a top bunk in a room with a guy trying to make early parole. He kept a Bible that he never opened at the foot of his bed so the guards would think he was a good guy, maybe pass the word along that he was getting his act together. He had a marijuana growing operation at his girlfriend's house down state, and wanted to get out in time for his harvest. We got along fine.

They served a lot of turkey there, maybe because it was cheap, maybe to keep the inmates good and drowsy, maybe both. Turkey stir fry. Turkey chili. Turkey sloppy joes. Turkey and egg breakfast burritos. You name it, it had once gone gobble-gobble. I spent most of my time in my bunk, dozing off, digesting, daydreaming.

One daydream in particular stands out. It might have actually been a dream, I can't remember. But I mulled it over, couldn't shake it, and it stuck with me when I got out and went back to my life. In spring, under that rickety porch, the fish would rot and fertilize the soil. Flowers would grow there. A great oak tree might even take root there, one that would rise up and split the house in two. I pictured it growing at a furious pace, like in Jack and the Beanstalk, knocking the actor off his feet, lifting him high into the air, where he'd wave his arms helplessly, rolling around a little like a turtle on its back, crying out in a squeaky voice that nobody on the ground could make out. Then I remembered the plastic bag that I'd wrapped the fish in, the little tidy bundle, the bag ready to biodegrade and release its fertilizer in a thousand or so years, though long before—probably already, in fact—it would be picked up, examined with a roll of the eyes and a shake of the head, and thrown in the trash.

LD VanAuken/Zombie Heart

*I am glad it cannot happen twice, the fever of first love. For
it is a fever, and a burden, too, whatever the poets may say.*
—from Du Maurier's *Rebecca*

There's always a second coming. The sequel
gone awry. It's set off by a scene in a movie,
a dead phone, a curled match. The without can be gasped,
like a bit of lint, right back in. So—*no*. I disagree.
Love can be an egg in the heart,
cracked by thaw. Or a butterfly turned pupa,
emerging back in. Even children know to fear
the wakeful dead: the troll that hobbles the bridge at noon,
the goblin that sulks in foggy bars. The man
who would not think to hurt you,
though you go at him with a cleaver and a cry.

Mary Carol Moran/Chambers Dictionary

Because it had a hard green cover,
   even though it was tiny, only
   two and a half by three inches,
and because my father had carried
   it, read it, held it in his breast
   pocket for four years, the cover
   wearing a little at the edges,
and because he had given it to me,
   a rare gift,
and because words were our blood
   bond, his PhD in structures
   of personal cognitive dictionaries,
   my inherited trust in the alchemy
   of who and why,
and because at seventeen I put it in a box
   and sent it to Denver with my college-
   bound books,
and because the post office lost the box,
   though I looked and asked and wrote,
   and he forgave, more he didn't need
   to forgive
because he understood,

since I was alone a thousand miles
   from home for the first time
and although or because I didn't miss home
since or because he wrote me letters
   about reading Piaget, grading
   freshman papers while watching
   the Cubs beat the Yankees or Gary
   Player win the Masters,
or perhaps because during World War II,
   at my age, he memorized the tiny
   dictionary, word by word, *abacus*

to *zymurgy*,
and because he practiced the words
   in his diary, causing the very candle
   of peace to flicker ominously,
   the diary I am now publishing,
and because words are the thread I hold,
   the yarn I unravel to knit
twenty-six years, the dictionary
   is as pliable and green
   as if I held it still,
and perhaps or because or since or although

   they are both lost,
   they are both gone,
   they are both here.

Ross Talarico/One

We try to live
a singular life. . .
One sun,
one moon,
one pair of hands cupped
over an object
of simple consternation.

I'm on this single road, in fact,
heading toward one big
empty house, a one-acre plot
to be exact
there in the heartland
where, from high in the atmosphere,
the endless rows of crops
would give anyone the impression
we are one, well-nourished planet.

What do I keep coming back to?
That feel of a baseball
hitting a wood bat squarely?
The dog's tongue on my neck?
Driving off the lot
in a brand new car?
There is a moment, surely,
that marks a sense of accomplishment:
a base hit, unconditional love,
material blessing!
But the house is still empty,
the driveway nothing but oil stains
on cracked and broken asphalt.

One song still beckons,
the one that requires my arm

around someone,
the convertible top down,
the summer night a blend
of warm pine and cigarettes.
We try and live a singular life,
the straight-forward proclamation
that equates dreaming with love. . .
Dream. . . dream, dream, dream
croon the Everly Brothers, their voices
whispering in the lines
along the electrical poles that filter
through the twilight of country roads.

And it is within that dream
that one's life passes.
In front of the mirror I see
what is left, what fell
from the smoky ceremonial and
took hold, the way one touches
one's own face and is astonished.

I never imagined such loneliness,
perfect stranger who talks me to sleep.
I never imagined how one crack
in the mirror before me
could separate a man from himself,
the concept of one so simplistic,
this sudden plea, like taking one's first step
in the midst of midnight's quake,
to open one eye, then the other.

Elena Karina Byrne/Bleach

Tell us, tell us—

there's a glacier ice chip melting in your mouth—name
what substance is in common (oh breathe)
with this absence so we can put our finger on it,
                    the white, white,
must-be probable cause, man against nature, camouflage
you wear when you don't want to be seen,
that bride-repeating petticoat edge
of eyelet, inconsequent
ceremony, and chaste ghost of chance when you knew
you had none.

Errata,

you are estranged down to the *écorché*,
feared saint set on fire.
Desolate as daydream: the object is losing its subject,
                    winter, its patience.
Zero, deliberately incomplete, now.
Rain carries no ink. Now and now
a downdraft of stars distance themselves from us,
the door loses its light where
the cold horizon comes phantom-alive in longing.

Hush, hush.

The mind holds out, cloud-poppy, everlasting
override. Plain speech, bible
of blank pages, petty speech, breech of color.

Erase,

the meadow lark's loom song, gone,

fog rack and stubblefield end-
line in the hour. Overturn
                        this act of silence, act of elegy. So:
fold open, unveil, and undo

the valediction of obedience. Yes: anxious
soothsayer, unknot
these sheets and lay out the stolen moth wings, jackpot bones
whose hues are bled invisible. . .
The new world will fall in on itself, your body's hiding place
                        will become sure
overture, pure sway and hum inside its beginning.
See the whites of their eyes?

        Do, do

and do stand back
because on the face of humanity's face
you don't have to recognize its final disappearing feature.

                Take the blame.

All things come from sadness.

        This *longing to be pure* is over.

Elena Karina Byrne/Crying

Boo hoo hoo

your opal stone drop-row of one alphabet wasted on
desire, the pantomime death.
                              Sky this.

Reach back as far as the human goes.
Grieving folly, of folly, man.

The crown coinage, salt chest, cuckoo's sorrow-flower pressed
under the dreaming head, is yours.

                         Stunt-growth this
emotion, eat daisy-root instead of deceit.

The lachrymal rivers fish out of the heart,
copious flow, if it rains
on this day.
                         Yes,
          once upon a time.

Muddled pond to guppies, mind-swim, and then there was a dry place
for Tyburn of old Paris, Greve, for
public executions.

                    Have we, what body's water, tear to tear?
As no witch would shed more than three tears,

you shall more than three million
make and weep, and wet.
And drink.

          So I say. So should you.

Jessica Stewart/Besotted

The dissonance of gasping bells released,
Priapic countenances flushed and tight.
Amid the luminescent specter's feast,
In deep illusion they imbibe tonight.
His sodden sabers poised, the eyes behold,
Tempestuous as beings bent and hazed.
Elusive, as the dawn's transcendent gold,
This appetizing pixie's hunter prays.
The bodies bend, the earth becomes opaque.
A sentient entity ascends in haste,
To coax the sweet quixotic heat awake.
The supple cloying nubile magic's taste.
The innocences languished to their ends,
For in the sacrifice a soul begins.

Gabriel Welsch/Make Your God an Ear

What does the birch in my yard
say to the rugosa? Anything
about roots? Or is the tree's
a hard won tolerance?

What would the iris say to the pear
that crowds its leaves
with a wayward branch? What
does anything really say?

Voices of trees are not deep
or loving or laced with language—
would it surprise us to learn
the voices keen a lament?

The voices of shoes are an endless sigh,
a gasp with each step.
The voices of empty rooms
echo laughter, nervous

and high, like children in a sudden dark.
The voice of the people is a thin wheeze,
aspirated and diffuse, sighed
until indistinguishable from a river or breeze.

Make God an ear, his spirit
the drum, the satellite, the thrumming
strand of silk, the carbide antenna
at the unseen end of a vast plane of sand,

the only thing to know air's abundance
of chatter and sigh, whisper and hum.

Bruce Douglas Reeves/MacBride with an "A"

None of us realized that afternoon when we paraded into Miss MacBride's class and discovered her posed like a Richard Avedon fashion model in front of her desk how eager she was for us, her twenty-six students, to like her. Because I'm near-sighted, I staked out a seat in the front row and had a chance to look her over while we waited for the bell to ring. Orange-lacquered nails gleamed on tanned fingers on either side of round hips a yard and a half from my nose. When I raised my gaze over the twin peaks of her bosom toward her yellow-brown irises she caught my eye and smiled, but I diverted my focus toward the other kids, most of whom I knew as acquaintances, if not as friends.

"This is sophomore English," she announced, her words coming across low and warm with the resonance that's the product of serious voice training. "My name—you see on the board—is Guinevere *Mac*Bride. I'm particular about the *a* in Mac. I don't like to get notes meant for Mr. McBride in Wood Shop and I doubt if he enjoys receiving *my* messages."

Arms folded so they pushed up her breasts, ankles crossed, striped skirt stretched over her thighs, she offered us a wide, somewhat wobbly smile. "This is the first year I've felt older than my students—I'm twenty-eight and you're, what, fourteen? There you are: I'm *twice* as old as you."

Nobody said anything on that first morning, but most of us were fifteen and a couple of fellows were sixteen. Kim Morganstern was thirteen, but she was a genius.

At first glance, Miss MacBride seemed to be a friendly female who'd be easy to get along with, but we soon sensed with the antennae that adolescents raise when confronting adults who have power over them that she was too anxious to pretend she was one of us. Even while insisting that kids in her classes were expected to bust their butts for grades, she giggled girlishly and leaned forward with little asides, as if she were one of the gang. She should've known you can't be both a hard taskmaster *and* a buddy.

"D'you think she meant that stuff about not giving A's?" Kim Morganstern whispered after class.

But the main topic in the hallway was Miss MacBride's hirsuteness. Although her heart-shaped face came close to being pretty, Guinevere MacBride's cheeks and upper lip obviously had been shaven and her arms were definitely shaggy. The inevitable remarks about "Monkey Woman" and "Hairy MacBride" were tossed out, but none of us had a reason yet to be aggressively malicious. That came a week later, when she returned our first essays.

Half the class flunked, and I was handed my first "C" ever. Whatever our past grades, we didn't meet *her* standards for English composition, and she was going to make sure we understood that.

"Jeez," moaned Angel Gomez, "what does that bitch want?"

"I know what she needs," growled Charlie Proctor. "But I ain't givin' it to her. A guy'd get lost in all that hair."

Miss MacBride appeared to erase her facial hair only once a week. We found it fascinating to watch the dark fuzz emerging day by day across her olive skin. Rosa Stimson wondered aloud in the cafeteria why she shaved her legs and face, but not her arms.

As we muddled through the initial skirmishes of the semester's educational wars, we were embarrassed more and more by the woman's coy flirtatiousness. Behind her back, the girls ridiculed her youthful skirts and sweaters and the way she flaunted her figure. The boys fluctuated in their feelings, resenting her most on her hairiest days. Without realizing it, we were disturbed by the contradiction between her abnormality and her conspicuously female shape and behavior.

We also had to deal with her philosophy of life.

If Miss MacBride believed in anything, it was *love*. According to her, every story we read, every poem, every play, conveyed the message that people should *love* each other. With the perverse stubbornness of adolescents, we resisted her message of kindness, understanding, and love, yet sometimes when she recited poetry she managed to transcend both her own eccentricities and the limitations of her audience. At those moments, the class unwillingly slid under her spell as her voice wove a tapestry of language and symbol, nuance and style. Squinting near-sightedly while she breathlessly read Alfred Lord Tennyson or Edna St. Vincent Millay, I gradually realized that Miss MacBride's power over the class's imagination was real and strong, and was based in equal parts on her passionate personality and her exotic hirsuteness.

A drama major in college, she'd nurtured fantasies of a stage career, but this dream soon had been channeled into the more realistic goal of making a living by teaching drama. Leaning against the blackboard, polishing the chalk tray with the back of her skirt, she reminisced about the year when she was a student teacher and helped high school kids scarcely older than she was produce *Our Town*. Her hope, she confided to the two dozen of us, was to teach drama again, but I wondered about her other aspirations that had been discouraged and frustrated. Did she still carry them locked within her, shielded from ridicule and pain?

On the last day before Christmas vacation, Miss MacBride told us we'd worked hard and deserved a break. She had us put away our books and then spent the next fifty minutes perched on the edge of her desk, ankles swinging, wide-cheeked face glowing, while she sang Christmas carols with us. The adolescent voices were as erratic as they were unsentimental, but it turned out she was a trained soprano who'd starred in amateur musicals and sung on the radio. Her *a capella* solo of "Ave Maria" reminded me of Jane Powell in old movies. She looked touchingly pleased when we showed we were impressed by her voice.

"If you have time during your holiday," she said, before we left the room, "turn your radios to KDYL during the Dill Riordan show. You might be surprised by what you'll hear." With a little coaxing, Miss MacBride confessed that she was a friend of the variety show host and was going to sing on his program. "When I told Dill I was a teacher," she admitted, with one of her kittenish giggles, tucking streaked brown locks behind one ear, "he said he wished *he'd* had teachers like me!"

In the hall, Charlie Proctor hissed, "Why would that guy've wanted a hairy teacher, for Chrissake?"

A spasm of anger made me want to punch Charlie, but, of course, I couldn't risk a reputation for defending Hairy MacBride. Also, I was mad at her in a way I hardly understood—perhaps because she made herself so vulnerable to the young barbarians who prowled the aisles of her class. It was as if she *wanted* us to hurt her. No adult, and especially not Guinevere MacBride, should be so naive. And I wondered about her relationship with this radio guy: did she go to bed with him? What right did a twenty-eight year-old female teacher have to a sex life?

Despite my mediocre beginning in her class, I worked like hell so that she broke her rule and awarded me an A-minus for the first quarter. Everybody in the class shared my pride in this victory. (Even Kim Morganstern only got a B.) However, in January when the final semester grades came out, my famous A-minus was erased by a B. Despite my youthful confidence, I hadn't been able to sustain my success. I stared at the blue letter vibrating on the yellow card. Miss MacBride had sabotaged me; her B knocked me off the Honor Roll.

The class gathered around, gaping at the bit of thin cardboard on my desk.

"The bitch," muttered Charlie Proctor.

"That's shitty," said Jack Langlois. "Really shitty."

Their own grades might've been involved. That B was an insult to the whole class. Now, I hated Miss MacBride more than I'd ever hated any teacher in my life—more than I'd hated any human being.

"Grades are only symbols," she reminded us, her words flying over our heads as we gathered up our books. She seemed to gasp for breath between sentences, undermining her statement: ". . .Remember, they mean nothing by themselves."

We didn't even acknowledge her as we left the room.

I labored diligently during the second semester, but with malice in my heart, challenging her, ridiculing her speeches about human decency and kindness, insisting that life was ugly and grim, that human beings were selfish and violent, and only saps believed in love.

Finally, on a steamy winter afternoon, Miss MacBride told me to stay after class. Twenty-five pairs of eyes glanced from her to me as they left the room. She silently erased the blackboard until they were in the hall, then she closed the door and walked to her desk, the clacking of her high heels on the composition tile floor like a drum roll before an execution.

"I know what you're trying to do," she said, "and I can't have it. I want to teach these kids some values."

She folded her orange-nailed hands on a stack of papers as she gazed down on me with those oversized brown eyes—a look, no doubt, she'd practiced in the mirror as a drama student.

I shrugged: "D'you want me to transfer to another class?"

Oily skin shining, an afternoon glow through the windows highlighting the stubble on her upper lip and chin, she foolishly let me see that she was surprised and hurt by my challenge.

"Don't be stupid," she snapped back. "Support me. You know you're the class leader. Don't waste that potential on petty differences between us. I *can* teach you a lot, if you'll let me. I'm a very good teacher." Maybe she was trying to manipulate me with flattery, but don't think I wasn't tickled to hear that admission and plea. "We'll talk again," she said.

She let me go, yet I wondered as I watched her hands fidget with a pencil on her desk which of us would win this battle—because, as far as I was concerned, a battle it continued to be. However, now, whenever I raised my hand to attack one of her inanities about love and life, she ignored me, and if I spoke without raising my hand, reprimanded me.

After a week of this, I marched to the Dean of Students and demanded he transfer me to another English class.

"A conflict of personalities," I complained. "And I'm not learning anything, anyway."

Dr. Hastings raised his white eyebrows and tapped his blotter with a blunt blue fingernail. Although he went through the motions of looking through schedules, the outcome was as preordained as the fact that this boring little man would be principal before his career ended: I couldn't transfer from Miss MacBride's class, he explained, without disrupting my entire schedule.

"No other sophomore English class is given at that hour," he told me. He sounded annoyed that Miss MacBride and I had complicated his existence.

The next afternoon, Miss MacBride ordered me to stay after class again.

"You two making love, or what?" whispered Charlie Proctor, as he slipped past my desk.

As soon as the room was empty, Miss MacBride slammed the door.

"You could've talked to *me* before going to Dr. Hastings," she said. "Instead of sneaking behind my back."

The vertical stripes of her green and yellow dress ballooned over her hips below a thin gold belt, her buttocks shifting nervously within the sleek fabric. I let my survey of the woman move across her breasts to her face. She needed a shave, but as her brown eyes focused on me a startling twinge of lust shot through my skinny limbs. I felt like a total pervert.

For an instant, she seemed to be silently pleading with me, but I refused to let any shards of sympathy penetrate my male pride. It occurred to me at that moment, with youthful egotism, that I might get her sacked. Her job, I reasoned, was more important to her than a grade was to me.

"I'm in school for an education," I said. "And I'm not learning any-thing in your class."

Stubbornly, I stared at the pictures of Tennyson and Byron and Laurence Olivier that she'd impaled on the bulletin board.

"That's too bad, because, young man, you have a *lot* to learn."

Our class together was the final one of the afternoon. We hurled words and emotions at each other for almost an hour, occasionally aware of the aimless enthusiasm of the baseball team practicing on the field outside. Gradually, I became aware of an odor in the room: female perspiration, *her* odor.

"I suppose you've missed your bus," she said, finally. I nodded. "I'll take you home, then."

Nervous that one of my friends would see us, I followed her to the faculty parking lot, but we met no one. Halfway across the macadam, I stooped to pick up a key and stuffed it into my pocket. I collected keys. You can find a lot of keys if you keep your eyes open.

The seat cover in Miss MacBride's old Chevy was torn and the floor littered with spent matches, empty cigarette packs, loose papers, and books. Without looking at me, she lit a Winston. This was the first time a teacher —any teacher, male or female—had smoked near me. I felt as if she'd done something indecent, as if by that single action all of my suspicions about her morals had been confirmed.

Puffing on her cigarette, she scattered ashes across her chest and lap as she guided the disreputable car across town. Paralyzed, I sat beside her, convinced that she was evil, not only because she smoked, but also because she was a woman and a sexual being and a creature who didn't know how to conceal these aspects of her existence. The hair on her face perversely exaggerated her womanliness. I knew I'd choke to death before we reached my house.

I couldn't decide if I should hate myself for my behavior or blame her for forcing me to act this way, but despite my bravado I felt guilty and ashamed—not that I would've admitted it to anyone.

After that day, an uneasy truce existed between Miss MacBride and me, but the rest of the class watched us with distrust. Then one afternoon during the last quarter, she ran into the room, threw her shapeless leather purse on her chair, and clasped her hands in front of her breasts.

"I'm going to have the drama classes!" she announced, breathlessly. "Next year. Mrs. Brogan is giving them up because rehearsals take her away from her family." Miss MacBride was so flushed and excited that, despite the perspiration glazing her forehead and chin, she looked young and pretty. "It's such an opportunity for me! I know there's a lot of talent in this school. And I have so much I can bring to it—together we can make something wonderful happen. You must try out for the play next year! *All* of you!"

I couldn't tolerate seeing Miss MacBride happy.

"What play? *The Hairy Ape*?"

She stared at me as if she'd been hit on the forehead by a rock. I couldn't believe I'd said those words. In fact, somewhere in my brain I hoped that I'd only imagined them and hadn't actually pronounced them aloud. But the silence in the room told me that I'd said them, all right, and would pay the consequences.

"No," she said, at last, her voice quivering, but as cold and deliberate as she could make it. "But I've been thinking about another O'Neill play: *Ah, Wilderness!* It's about a boy who's too smart for his own good."

The bell rescued the rest of the class, yet she gestured for me to stay in my chair. When she turned from closing the door, I saw tears trembling between the red rims of her yellow-brown eyes. I'd never made a woman cry before.

"I wish you *could* get out of my class," she said, breasts heaving, head tilted back as if to keep the tears from spilling out of their precarious pools. "I *want* you out of my class."

She snatched her purse and stomped gracelessly toward the door, but the leather strap swung loose from her arm, and the purse hit the wall. Falling open, it poured its contents across the checkerboard-patterned floor. She looked at me with hatred in her eyes: no tears, now, just hatred.

I knelt to help her gather up cosmetics and tissues, keys, and other junk. She snatched a small package from under a chair and stuffed it into the depths of the handbag, but not before I glimpsed the Kotex label. Beneath the bleached hair on her cheeks, her skin burned red. As I returned a fistful of loose change, my hand brushed against her shaggy arm, a shiver crossing my body.

She snapped shut the heavy purse and gave me a long, silent gaze. I don't know what she was thinking or feeling, but at that moment she struck me as pitifully vulnerable and alone. Suddenly, I was shocked by the gratuitousness of my actions. Then, without another word or gesture, she left me in the classroom, twenty-eight vacant chairs condemning me.

The end of the term finally rescued us, summer passed too quickly, and then our lives were launched across yet another school year. I was worried I'd be assigned to Miss MacBride's junior English class—school administrators often were guilty of such perverse actions—but discovered when I picked up my schedule that fat and friendly Mr. Cibber was stuck with me for the year.

I hadn't even considered enrolling in one of Miss MacBride's drama classes and managed to avoid her during the first weeks of the fall semester. When we finally did pass in the hall, I didn't know where to look, but she nodded and said, "Hello," as if we'd never been enemies. Nevertheless, I wouldn't have auditioned for the "Evening Off Broadway" she was planning if she hadn't stopped by me in the cafeteria one day to invite me to try out.

"You used to recite poetry beautifully in my class," she said.

The tooled leather purse hung from her shoulder, summer-tanned fingers resting on the wide flap. I looked at her across my half-eaten hamburger, trying to figure out why she was being so nice. Then I realized, as I tried to think what to say and searched her face for a clue, that she *liked* me. Despite everything I'd done, a connection existed between us, a bond that she seemed to want to preserve. I shrugged and told her that I'd think about it. Behind me, Charlie Proctor snorted.

"Go ahead," he urged, after she left. "I *dare* you to try out."

Pretending that I didn't care if I got a part or not, on the last afternoon of auditions I dropped by the Little Theater and read a few speeches. I decided I'd be willing to take on the Gentleman Caller in the scene from *The Glass Menagerie* that made up a third of the program, but she gave me the bit part of the nerdy tax collector in the *You Can't Take It With You* scene. The funny thing was, I wasn't even pissed off about it. Maybe I couldn't make up for what I'd done last year, but I'd show her I could be a good sport.

The combined casts for the scenes from the Tennessee Williams and Kaufman and Hart plays and the O'Neill one act were large and restless during the evening rehearsals. While Miss MacBride directed one scene, kids from other scenes roamed backstage, around the theater, and up and down the halls, waiting for their turns on stage. Pleas that they sit quietly at the back of the Little Theater were spectacularly ineffective.

Miss MacBride's efforts to control the kids soon degenerated into a series of temper tantrums alternating with speeches about why we should be good citizens instead of rowdy hoodlums. None of the adolescent actors were impressed by either her impassioned appeals or her shrill anger. Each night, the kids not on stage wandered through the school, necked in empty classrooms, played games in the halls, and disrupted late choir and band rehearsals.

Piggy Strahorne, the Vice Principal, heard about the nightly commotion and, with his customary light touch, reduced Miss MacBride to tears. She, in turn, screamed at the cast, but their behavior didn't improve. Finally, Piggy sat in on a rehearsal, himself. That evening, while he squatted in the rear of the Little Theater cleaning his fingernails with a penknife, everyone managed to behave, but the night of the dress rehearsal Angel Gomez threw a chair at Mike Celello, missing Mike but sending it through one of the plate glass cafeteria windows.

After that, Piggy damn near cancelled the whole show, but Miss MacBride pacified him by announcing that Angel, who was playing the Gentleman Caller in *The Glass Menagerie*, wouldn't go on. Somebody else would take his part, reading the lines from the script. The rest of the cast protested that she was being unfair, but she said that after what we'd done we were lucky Mr. Strahorne let us go ahead with the show. She asked me if I'd read the part, since I was familiar with it, yet I shook my head. In the end, Ronnie Kimmel read it and did a pretty lousy job of it, too.

Monday after the final performance, Miss MacBride called a cast meeting—to discuss the cast party, we thought. Most of us were in the room when she walked in, wearing a high-necked red dress against which her hirsute shadow contrasted unpleasantly.

"Don't worry," she began, "there isn't going to be a cast party for *this* group. In my entire experience in drama, I've never worked with such an undisciplined, rowdy bunch of so-called actors. Haven't you *any* pride?" She hesitated and the only sounds were Angel Gomez cracking his knuckles and Lana Roth fidgeting in her purse. "It was bad enough that we had to have a substitution for one of the major roles, but some of you didn't even know your lines. Unless you were deliberately flubbing to embarrass me —and I wouldn't put that past any of you. The audience probably thought it was *my* fault. It's not something to giggle about, Lana. And please do me the courtesy to not apply makeup while I'm talking."

She stopped and, turning her back on us, walked over to the chalkboard and stared at it for a moment, before continuing. When we saw her face again, it glistened with perspiration and the brown of her eyes was screened behind a liquid film.

"To think that Mr. Strahorne had to come to rehearsals to enforce discipline! And that window! I've never been so humiliated. You all should be ashamed of yourselves—doing this to me!"

"So what've you done for *us*?" demanded Angel Gomez. "As a teacher?"

Miss MacBride stared at us, then turned and waved toward the door with her hand. We filed out, embarrassed for her, as much as for ourselves.

We had a cast party, anyway, without Miss MacBride, at Lana Roth's house.

For the next few months, I was busy with classes and my own life, such as it was. That spring, Miss MacBride directed an old murder mystery, *Night Must Fall*, for the annual play. I didn't have anything to do with it, but I heard stories about what went on during the auditions, when she made a speech telling everybody who tried out that some of them were bound to be disappointed, but she hoped they'd still support the play.

"I wanted roles when *I* was in school," she said. "Many times, I knew I could perform a role better or sing better than the girl chosen, but if the director had a little blonde in mind, a little blonde got the part. Talent isn't always enough."

No one was clear what message she was trying to get across, but, of course, some of the students who read for parts *were* disappointed—including several of the most popular and powerful kids in the school. Frank Evensen, student body president and California state speech champion, had expected to play Danny, the murderously charming lead, and his sidekick Dick Troutman assumed he'd get the role of the inspector who traps Danny. As far as they were concerned, *Night Must Fall* belonged to them. They were so sure Miss MacBride would give them the parts that they didn't even hang around to watch the other auditions. But Hairy awarded the leads to a pair of boys no one had considered competition: Billy Marek, a cocky loner that nobody knew much about, and Joe Stamp, a fat misfit notorious for his foul breath and raspy voice.

Once again, Guinevere MacBride demonstrated her ability to alienate the maximum number of students.

Frank and his gang—including Bliss Tuckerman, Alan Jarvis, and Norm Murasaki, presidents of the three most important social clubs — steadily and energetically ridiculed the play and everyone involved with it. You'd hear them in the cafeteria at noon and at the Creamery after school, laughing at Hairy and her cornball mystery and its cast of misfits. Despite my own grievances toward Guinevere MacBride, I felt a growing pity as I watched the campaign against her production.

The week before opening night, Frank Evensen and Dick Troutman, who were also editor and cartoonist of the school *Reporter*, mimeographed a fake edition filled with articles and cartoons satirizing *Night Must Fall*.

When we arrived at school in the morning, the mock papers were already distributed on every desk. I ran into Miss MacBride in the hall between classes. Her damp brown eyes stared into me, and I averted my near-sighted gaze from her recently depilated chin.

"Why do they hate me?" she asked.

The dirty tricks didn't end with the fake edition of the school paper. The morning of the day the play was to open, we discovered that beards and masses of hair had blossomed on each of the photographs attached to the posters publicizing the play, so it looked as if it had been cast with a tribe of werewolves.

Night Must Fall's three-night run attracted twenty-eight people for the first performance, twenty-one the second night, and exactly thirteen people the final night. I know, because I went to all three performances and counted. On that last evening, I turned around and saw Miss MacBride sitting in solitary misery at the back of the almost empty theater. For some reason, I felt as if *I* were responsible for the fiasco.

After the show, as I was waiting for a city bus under the only street lamp not smashed, Miss MacBride drove up in her battered Chevy.

"Get in," she said. "I'll take you home." A couple of blocks later, she lit a Winston, dropping the paper matchbook onto the mess on the floor. "You know I smoke," she said. "And I need it."

A yellowish street light briefly illuminated her face, her shaggy arm, and the smoke from the cigarette curling inside the car. This woman, I realized, had taught me more than any other teacher—more than I wanted to know. She'd taught me so much that I was afraid of her, but at the same time as we drove through the cool night, I felt a man, stronger than the woman beside me—almost her protector. We didn't say much as we bounced across town in the corroded Chevy, but she seemed calmer when she dropped me off in front of my house.

I twisted the loose doorhandle, jiggled it, and the door flew open, a couple of empty cigarette packs falling to the pavement. I turned back and looked at Miss MacBride, who seemed to be in a trance, staring at the filthy windshield. Then she raised her eyes in my direction and managed a bit of a smile. She was clutching the steering wheel so tightly that she might've been trying to keep the thing from flying out of the car like a murderous discus.

"Thank you," she said, the two words enunciated with terrifying clarity.

Only a few weeks of my junior year remained, weeks occupied with finals and school elections. I ran for Student Body Treasurer but lost to Lee Ann Simpson—Frank Evenson's girlfriend. The kids still talked about what Hairy needed. We all said that if Hairy MacBride had a man she'd relax and go easier on her students. We also joked about the courage needed by any man who dared make love to her.

Angel Gomez told me to be sure to drop by drama class on the last day of school. Something special was going to happen. So I was seated at the back of the Little Theater, where the drama class was held, when Lana Roth stood up and announced that the class wanted to say something. Miss MacBride nodded.

Lana said that the drama students had talked it over and felt ashamed for the bad time they'd given her during the year, so they wanted to give her a present. Lana held out a package. Miss MacBride was really pleased. I could tell from the back of the room how pleased she was, but I had a premonition as she fumbled and ripped the silver paper off the box, the blue ribbon coiling over her fuzzy wrist.

I half-rose in my seat, squinting as I tried to see what was happening. Everybody was staring silently at Miss MacBride as she opened the box. Her face twisted and she dropped the package, running from the room. I heard her crying as she lumbered down the hall.

Pushing my way to the front of the room, I looked at the box on the floor. Beside it, on the torn silver paper and blue ribbon, lay a Gillette safety razor.

That summer, I worked downtown in the stockroom of a variety store that had been around since before the Depression. It was lousy job and the old guy who ran the place was a grumpy bastard, but it paid pretty well—at least for a kid just turning seventeen. Sometimes, I had to work late, into the evening, but I didn't have anything else I needed to do, and I was saving everything I earned toward college.

It was after one of those late shifts, as I made my way down one of the dark side streets toward my bus stop, that I heard her voice. Although the kids all talked about Miss MacBride's appearance, she had a distinctive voice, low and mellow—the trained tones of a singer and actress, I guess. She sounded upset, as if she was crying, or had been, which seemed strange at ten o'clock at night, but it was her, all right. She and whoever she was with were on the other side of a square brick column at the entrance to Lorenzo's Corner Bar & Café. I hesitated next to the brick wall, not sure what to do.

"Don't go to New York without me, Dill," she said. "Don't leave me here."

I couldn't make out what he replied, but it was embarrassing, standing on the street, listening to Miss MacBride begging. They moved on around the corner, voices rising and falling. I followed as far as the spot where they'd been standing, then peeked around the edge of the building. An old streetlamp that hadn't been smashed sent a dim amber light over the two of them. They went on down the block, and I backtracked, going the long way to my bus stop.

When school started in the fall, I wondered if Miss MacBride would be teaching again. Did that Riordan guy take her to New York? Or did she follow him, hoping he'd relent once she was there? The desperation I'd heard in her voice had shocked me. I hoped I wouldn't see her again, that she was three thousand miles away, but two days after the beginning of my senior year I saw Guinevere MacBride coming down the hall toward me in that striped green dress. She asked how my summer had been. I mumbled something about working most of my vacation.

"Good for you," she said. "I know you're going to have a bright future. Don't get so busy with your senior year activities that you forget to try out for the play this year. I'm counting on you old timers to help me out."

And, bulky leather purse swinging from its long strap, she strode off down the corridor.

Tom Chandler/Lascaux

The plot still unfolds from left to right,
an ancient comic strip in stone
still thicker than a blood clot.

Sixteen thousand years have passed
inside a single minute, but the bison's
horns are still sharp as hunger

and the dancing shaman's handprints
still as intricate as fossiled ferns,
each whorl where he carefully pressed his fingers

unmatched by anyone born before or since,
as if he is still trying to tell us
just exactly who he thought he was.

Rachel Kann/Arboretum Canticle

I

let me show you,
here is the shape of this love:
in my hand,
a snapped branch
white as marrow inside.
the scent, clean as anything.

i press the twig to the soft
grit of moist earth,
scrape out a circle
where i keep your secrets.

II

you panic at the sight of
your open palms.

i am all asylum.
this, i promise to every last
quiver and nervous
handed over.

i fold my skirt up to hold them.
their weight, shape,
embed your history into my thighs,
letterblocks in a printing press.

i mean to be
as much like trunk
as torch can be.
sturdy and planted,
that you may lean to me.

III

the intimate burden of legacy.
the abrupt and whine and gasoline
of chainsaw against chaste wood.

strangefruit
stays everlodged in your throat.

the rope, an indelible necklace
i have learned to work into my repertoire.

IV

i have dislodged,
shaken the soil,
all that anchors.

whittled down to
a leaping faith incarnate.

let me show you,
i'll shake this autumn from my hair.

believe in the promise beneath.

Jed Myers/ Where We Stand

As if I'd sensed the soft rain's hold
all night, I slept through, the quiet
house itself soothed, I guess
I felt, in that cool mist,

until I rose to see the glisten
out the window on the grass,
the moss, the crowded balconies of leaves,
then recalled one scene—

the narrow platform between
a hissing train on its track and the brick
station, where we stand, in what seems
an arid country, the same
flatness in all directions, and no wind—

a land near-dead of thirst, baked
hard and cracked. Our cases,
tightly packed, wait beside us
in the heat like obedient dogs.
We're not sure this train is ours.

Ashley M. Carrasco/Butterfly Within

I dread going home
To that dark crowded room,
Where you deeply sleep,
to the clock's tic tocks.

As I watch you slumber,
I think to myself:
I am a caterpillar
Stuck in a box.

No windows, no walls,
No doors, no chairs—
Just a hole at the top,

And a single rope,
Taunting me. Dangling,
Too far to reach. . .
I need escape!

Far, far, far away—

Where clouds are pink,
And grass purple.
No storms of cries—
Just a simple melody.

The key to my brain,
The treasures I clasp,
Grub as the blueprint,
Labor as my ecstasy.

But, eeegh, for now,
These 16 legs must do,
Until that spring day,
When fancy-free I fly.

Barbara Rockman/Soon, My Mother Will Die

The season is designed with dark letters.
Eaves guttered with wet leaves
and the rank wit fall offers.

Like her, slack skinned, it stretches
a thin hand over root-ridged paths,
to the lake which,

like a polished plate, waits
for decoration, for its edges
to be trellised with gold leaf and ash.

Lake of the last house,
motherless and unafraid,
luminous like her creased cheek.

Like leaves flattened to the soles of my shoes,
the imprint of her long walk presses into mine.

Maple-tinged sky so clear
it might be lying.

Robert Guard/Grounded

Every knot has an answer,
Its cats cradle of knuckled under,
Twisted 'round the other.

Take this angel, bound here
By accident, blooming red
On the horizon.

Crouching and knowing
The nature of nature,
You plant all that you have.

Knowing hillsides
And the blue ceilings they suffer,
Can take you anywhere you want to go.

Now these bony hills escape you,
Bleeding your hands and knees.
When this rise is given over

To rhododendrons, the heart thinks,
Love will have its stranglehold.
Then, you too will take root.

Robert Guard/Heartland

There are no tears in the eye of a tornado;
Stillness reigns in a light the color of steel.

A farmhouse spins, weathered above
The absence of foundation.

The wife inside, baking bread, kneads her hands
In a swirl of leaves and laundry.

Outside the men gather lengths of chain,
To bind whatever they can.

Brad Johnson/Racist

It's become impossible for me to say the word nigger.
Even when teaching Faulkner.
In "That Evening Sun" young, white Jason asks Nancy "Am I a
    nigger?"
He doesn't know what the word means.
He is taught.
Toni Morrison forgives Hemingway his racism because she loves his
    books.
This does not always assuage my students.

A black man driving a white car.
A white man driving a black car.

I told my friend I was standing in front of Dunkin' Donuts.
Next to the black guy.
The black guy insisted he wasn't black but African-American.
I've been corrected by Haitians after calling them African-Americans.
They're Haitians they tell me.

A white man standing in front of a black door.
A black man standing in front of a white door.

I have a black neighbor, black friends, black co-workers.
They tell me black is okay.
They call me their white neighbor, white friend, white co-worker who
    never holds the elevator.
The man in front of Dunkin' Donuts insists black is not okay.

A black man yelling at a white man.
A white man yelling at a black man.

I said I have black friends.
We've lost touch.
Should I be looking for replacement black friends?
If it's racist to not like a person for their skin color, is it racist to want a

friend for their color?

A black man living in a white house.
A white man living in a black house.

Being branded racist is being branded witch, communist, terrorist.
I've read *The Autobiography of Malcolm X* but am not a Muslim.
I've blasted Public Enemy's "Fuck tha Police" at stoplights with my
    windows down.
I'll never visit Alabama because I'm afraid of the crazy white people.

A white man approaching a black family.
A black man approaching a white family.

Can I use the word nigger when demonstrating how words have
    historical punch and contextual meaning?
Should I really refer to it as the N-word like some eight-year-old
    swearing without swearing with the F-word, the S-word?

A white man teaching black students.
A black man teaching white students.

Next week my class is reading Gloria Steinem and Anne Sexton.

Toni Fuhrman/Spoils

"Gwen, this is Hatch. Hatch, Gwen."

Gwen's husband left her a few weeks before to live with a woman Gwen described as "that anorexic airhead blonde he hired a year ago." Molly, her grown-up stepdaughter, had come by with her boyfriend to pick up her father's things.

They stood in the hallway of Gwen's house while Hatch rubbed his hands together, cold from the biting wind off Lake Michigan, and blew on them before he held out his hand to her. Gwen hesitated, then took it. He squeezed until she responded with a small, reluctant smile.

"Hatch came along to help me," said Molly. "Dad thought it would be easier this way."

"Help yourselves," said Gwen. "What's his is yours."

Molly, who was trying not to take sides, sighed and went out to the car to get empty boxes. Gwen and Hatch stood facing each other.

"The bedroom is upstairs and to the right," said Gwen.

Hatch nodded, crossing his arms under his broad chest.

"Shall I show you the way?" said Gwen peevishly.

"I'd like that," said Hatch. He was a big man, impressively tall. His hair was light brown, almost blond. He was older than Molly, and younger than Gwen.

Gwen turned away, marching ahead of him up the stairs. Her buttocks were tight against her jeans, her hair slightly damp against her neck. She heard him breathing lightly behind her. Standing at the doorway of the bedroom, she ushered him in, her arm extended dramatically. Hatch smiled and walked past her, brushing against her as if accidentally.

He looked around the room at the four-poster bed, the massive chest of drawers, the old-fashioned dressing table, the open closet door with her husband's suits and sport jackets hanging in a neat row.

"You're not sleeping in here," he said.

"No. Neither is my husband."

"Ah. I see."

"Like hell you do," said Gwen. "And what's it got to do with you?"

For answer, Hatch leaned against the chest of drawers, looking at her. His eyes moved down her body and up again to her face.

She flushed. Something shifted inside her. She took a few steps into the room and glanced around as though, like Hatch, she were seeing it for the first time.

"What's your last name?" she said abruptly, walking around the bed to the window. She adjusted the curtains, which were puffing slightly in the cold wind.

"Hatcher."

"Your name is Hatch Hatcher?"

"That's right."

"That's like being called Woody Woodpecker."

He smiled but didn't respond. They stood on either side of the bed and looked at each other. The bed anchored them in place. They could hear the wind.

"Are you in love with Molly?" she said.

"Yes," he said.

"Does my husband know?"

"Yes. He approves."

She was bristling, every hair on her body standing at attention.

"How long have you known her?"

"Long enough."

Gwen's laugh sounded harsh, even to herself.

"Hatch? Hatch!" Molly called.

Still looking at Gwen, Hatch called back, "Yeah, babe."

"Come help me with these boxes, will you?" Her voice floated up from the bottom of the stairs.

"I'm on my way," said Hatch.

Turning away from him as he walked out of the bedroom, Gwen knew with a sudden fierce intensity that she would be merciless when she took him from Molly, "pretty Molly," "sweet Molly," her husband's only child, loved by him, petted, protected, not shunned, discarded. She could hear them laughing as they struggled with the empty boxes. She liked the sound of his laugh. It was big, like him, and unselfconscious. They murmured to each other as they climbed the stairs, the brief, unfinished exchanges of intimacy.

Gwen walked to the dressing table and leaned over it to look at herself in the mirror. The old beveled glass distorted her image slightly as it reflected the sweep of her hands through her hair, the heightened color in her face, the taut pressure of her nipples against her T-shirt. She backed away and continued to look in the mirror until she could see the two of them reflected behind her.

John McKernan/My Purchase of the Brooklyn Bridge

I bought it the day of my first orgasm and have occasionally
      regretted the transaction

I first thought of buying it when I was 12 and every year
      after until I was 6

I bought it because it looks like a cathedral and reminds me
      of the one on 40th Street in Omaha

The day I bought it I saw my father float from his grave and
      surf down the suspension cables

He said "Some things on Earth only seem to last forever   Take
      bigger gulps of air   Don't wait up for me"

The bridge came equipped with a ten year supply of Egyptian
      hieroglyphs and a lifetime run on Greek poems

I have heard many times the Atlantic whisper through its
      translating cables but I choose not to believe it when
      it says DIE   DIE   DIE   DIE

Surprising to say I like it better as a black and white photo
      It gives me the sense it is never going to go away

The man with beads the man with a red-yellow skin the
      man who smiled the man who sang a lullaby to the
      color black the man who sold it to me spoke of his
      trip by foot on ice across the Bering Sea kept saying
      It is worth   It is worth much   It is worth much more

It cost me four weeks of *The Omaha World Herald* route
      number 134 profits

I bought it in December   I could feel its cold concrete rock
        steel girders and cables   Rows of doves like strands
        of pearl on each gleaming cable

I will never sell it

It's mine

I bought it after listening to a hundred people in one day using
        sign language tell me "There is certainly no God"   The
        adverb *certainly* in sign language is a joy to behold

Several people have recently committed suicide each with
        a copy of Hart Crane in their book bags or purses

A speeding ticket on the Brooklyn Bridge always reminds me
        of what I wanted out of life

I have purchased the Brooklyn Bridge at least seven times

I bought it to see the blast furnaces in Wheeling and Gary
        spin its molten cable threads

I bought it for the graffiti and the sound of the tugboats in fog

I bought it to sniff the different flavors of stone dust from
        the stone mason's rock drill

I bought it to prove that Beauty can cross a void

I bought it to look at a blueprint from different angles

I bought it to understand those who urge the universe has no
        blueprint

I bought it to examine the thesis that one's theory of bridges
        is one's theory of life

I bought it to use as a grave marker

I bought it because it is as far away from Hollywood as one can drive

I bought it to remind myself there are always two shores

I bought it   I would have bought two

I bought it because regret does rhyme with threat

Once for a song

Once with a stolen credit card

Twice with forged checks

Once with a shoplifted bottle of communion wine

One time through the mail

Now and then I see little tufts of grass or a cranny of
        wild flowers sprout from chinks in a stone buttress

At least one hawk lives on the cables to thank the fish
        and the smaller birds

In America   Motion is a new form of standing still

Because this Earth has plenty of fill dirt in it

Because it was the first thing in America my grandfather
        looked at

Because the Roebling Brothers (John and Washington)

probably saw my Irish grandparents tumble off
the boat in New York Harbor

Because a crane is not enough and Earth was once a scoop of
"our" sun

Because the Bridge can attract lightning from a cloudless sky
and the traffic goes both ways

Because few have climbed to the top and it provides excellent
training for Mount Everest

If its left lane points towards Stonehenge its right lane points
at the Nile

Because it is hard to see the tin cups and the squeegees
of Manhattan

Because Nebraska is west of Brooklyn and I love the sound of
the word *insatiable*

Because some poems deserve translation but most sunlight
resists even transcription

Because I have seen people sleeping in January in its stone
corners

Because a bridge is a constant way of thinking even when
covered with snow

Because history is not a comma or a form of spelling since
many fled west to Kansas and Utah

Because I needed to drown my fear of heights

Because I love to look down at my reflection in the summer
sky on the sunlit water   The shimmering rays of light
surrounding the shape of my skull

Because when a snowflake steps into the East River it never
said "Now I feel at home"

Because these stones are not the kindergarten of nothingness
or a compass needle pointed south

Because when the wool is pulled over one's eyes all that
remains is dream and memory

Because what else is there?

Because a bird can fly forwards and backwards and sideways
but not at the same time

Because wine does not rhyme with urine

Because I would break every sundial and every empty plate
to distinguish myself from a marsh pond and its spool of
eels for a brain

Because a bridge is both text and alphabet

Because as the gray one says "Nothing else is more spiritual"

I bought it because I was hungry and I wanted to see it in fog

I bought it because no bridge is a prison

I bought it to calculate the cost of joy and the price of faith

I bought it in an ice storm and waited for the glaze of sunlight
to remove its cold mirror

I bought it because it points toward Chicago and the Eiffel
Tower stretches toward the clouds

I bought it for its view of Ireland to increase my forgetfulness
as a home remedy

I bought it to insult and bring low my fears

I bought it to make my grave seem distant

I bought it because it can improve a dawn and dissolve some
        sunsets

I bought it to read my name and learn my place

I bought it as a substitute for empty space where people have
        sex on it all hours of the day and night

Who is the police officer whistling at?   The jet from Newark?
        The idle swimmer?   The fish and eel below?

I bought it to hear the explosive blast in the granite quarry

To smell the diesel fuel of the museum house earth loaders
        and the iron ore trucks near Hibbing Minnesota

I bought it because beauty is sex's voice coach and I will some
        day want to sell it to you

Tanya Stepan/If I Could Kill

If I could kill want.
If I could kill heresy & hesitation, the righteous,
& the nonbelievers,
and the girl who will betray us.
If I could kill the damn barking dog,
the computer's hum.
Kill fine linen and rotten corpses.
If I could kill exoneration,
placation, unwanted hair so he could suck me better.
If I could kill the overflowing billow that was her dress.

Jim Daniels/Thaw, Freeze

Footprints on the trail iced over.
Photos stuck together

random in a shoebox.
We repeat ourselves by saying

history repeats itself. History
shovels coal into the furnace, cussing

at whoever's upstairs complaining.
Which would be us.

Learning to sew would have been
useful. As would having a pet to blame.

No big thing today to be recorded
in the books and *tsked* over.

Just lonely bones slipping on ice.
Nobody's feet fitting the glass slippers.

Jim Daniels/Desperation for Eternity

The clock windy, and the rain percussive.
The dog strummed a giant guitar in his dreams.
Romance changed its name to Jade Cynic.
The one green plant collapsed in a heap.
Snow, an instrument of denial and worship.
God was in the details, and he wasn't coming out.
Darkness said, *Just call me Dark.*
Bags of groceries interrupted the proceedings.
Bribery was attempted, then judged by a bribed panel.
Hair cut and collected, then set on fire.
Decency flew out the door, down the street, then called in sick.
The big eye closed, and everyone went home disappointed.
We punctured the lifeboats and had a good laugh.
We held up numbers to rate our final days.

Ginny Lowe Connors/A Book, a Bird, A Question

"The valise opens and a bird rides out on the wind"
—Nance Van Winckel

Your eyes change daily, blue to green
and back, like a pebble I once held, entirely made of sea.

What's constant—our foolishness, its warp and weft,
its dailiness. If you'd weave from it a blanket,

it would become my only comfort. Instead
you leave your book of numbers open near my chair

and whistle yourself away. A traveler lifts his hand
to knock. Home, he says, is what you must leave

in order to feel its currents, its unrelenting draw.
And then he sighs, drops his scuffed leather case.

The valise opens and a bird rides out on the wind
through a door that bangs open again and again.

The curve of its flight unfurls like sail or memory,
circles back and hangs in the air for one

long moment as it wonders at fire in the window.
Everything leaves us, even the sun. And dusk

is an animal with dark, moist eyes. It comes this close,
but is never quite tamed. The whiteness of a single tree,

unreeling its bark at twilight, is it a reflection? You shrug.
It hardly matters. The number of atoms in the universe

does not alter. But I want to know, if you look for me
a thousand years from now, where will I be?

Ginny Lowe Connors/Wheat Field with Crows

Vincent van Gogh

From fields lush with wheat
they rise up, those old black
sorrows, crying out my name,
taking pleasure in it too. Like the stiff
straw men abandoned there,
coming unhinged, they flap
and stir the chaff to storms
of golden dust. What crooked rut
is this that wanders, a little green,
into the grain toward
the squawking of crows?
Even when I believe I've left
the world's restless errands behind,
an agitation follows me.
In this incandescent world
the sky comes roiling closer,
bearing again its difficult night.

David Hovhannisyan/Yankee Rose

Indulgence, not compulsion.

Abandon hope and let addiction reign,
to cleanse suspended curiosity,
when simple questions ravish anxious pain.

Oblivious retention tempts the sane,
directing trails of animosity,
abandon hope and let addiction reign.

Descend the steps and taste a beggar's strain,
as anger teases generosity,
when simple questions ravish anxious pain.

Subdued awareness terminates disdain,
provoking sensitive ferocity,
abandon hope and let addiction reign.

Decline possessions sober men attain,
and show discretion no atrocity,
when simple questions ravish anxious pain.

Impulsive actions breathe to entertain,
discharging blood with new viscosity,
abandon hope and let addiction reign,
when simple questions ravish anxious pain.

Tyrone Jaeger/Woe to You, Destroyer (Who Yourself Have Not Been Destroyed)

for Rabbit and Sissy

Humping a grease-spattered backpack, GI entered the east side of Cheesman Park. Two men, his friends, followed, and Nellie, pushing a shopping cart, brought up the rear. A morning breeze washed over the park, and they walked to the Grecian pavilion that had once offered a panorama of Denver, a view now blocked by cottonwoods and condos. A century before the park had been a cemetery, and some said that the ghosts of those dead that had been dug up and transferred elsewhere still haunted. GI thought of himself as a kind of ghost, a shadow of a former, half-forgotten self.

A hundred-year heat wave bore down on Denver. Dried rose bushes with chapped and puckered blossoms, dead grass, and yellowed cottonwoods surrounded the pavilion. The ground ached for water. "Let's stop and have a nip," GI said. Chico and Ted set their backpacks on the pavilion floor and leaned against them. GI pulled out the remains of last night's bottle, and Nellie sat down, her back to him.

"I don't want to stay no more where we did last night," Nellie said.

"No one asked you to go in there with him," Chico said.

"Nellie," Ted said, "we should call you Martyred Mother of Our Cause."

"I'll tell you two to shut it just once," GI said. He handed the bottle to Nellie. Yesterday, after Ted had struck it big—a fifty-dollar bill—holding a sign, they had visited Julius's apartment, smoked grass, and slept in his air-conditioned living room. Nellie had bartered with Julius, and no one had stopped her when she followed him into his bedroom. GI hadn't slept, not even after Nellie had finished and she had curled up on the floor beside him. They had left before Julius woke, and Ted still had most of the fifty.

In the pavilion, Nellie now sang, "Happy birthday to you, happy birthday dear Tommy."

Chico rolled a thin cigarette. He said, "This is the fourth birthday that kid's had in about as many weeks."

"Shut it," GI said.

"It's no use encouraging her delusions," Chico said.

Nellie stood and looked down on Chico. "You're the only delusion I see." She closed and opened her eyes, and then snarled at Chico for refusing to disappear. They watched as Nellie pushed her cart off the pavilion and across the road that snaked through the park and into the mown field below. She pulled a blanket from the cart, spread it on the grass, and removed her jacket. The men continued to drink from the bottle but found it hard to remove their gaze from Nellie. "You're finding out like I did," Chico said. "The hard way."

"She only did it for us. Don't try to bring her down." GI's voice was deep and scratched. He rolled a cigarette. The rising sun infected the sky with the oranges and yellows of cancer. "I shouldn't of let her do it."

"That's what I'm getting at, bro," Chico said. "You think you got a hold on what she does." GI handed Chico the rolling papers and the tobacco. "She does what she wants to do, and you can't be thinking she's doing something *for* you. That ain't the way that gal works. And I—"

"Should know," GI said. "How many times *you* told me that?"

"Relax, fellahs," Ted said. "You ruining the only pleasant time of day." He pulled on his smoke-stained gray moustache. "Now look at that sweet lady." Nellie's shirt was rolled to the base of her breasts, sun shining on her belly and legs, both browned like cigar paper. "Dear Martyred Mother," Ted said.

GI tossed his cigarette. Smoke slowly vented from his mouth and nose, lingering about his head as if his insides smoldered. He burned for Nellie. Her refusal to honestly love him back sparked his shame. She had little regard for herself and certainly none for him. She did what she wanted—she was prideful and vain—*and* she stayed by his side. A study in contradiction. GI wondered if he loved her more because she loved him less, loved him with an inconsistency that gave him headaches.

Last night, she had traded herself so that they might sleep safely. There was the heat, yes, but more threatening were the murders—serial murders committed against Denver's homeless. GI, Nellie, Chico, and Ted had been sleeping together under the Federal Bridge—GI believed in the safety of numbers. They didn't need to stay at Julius's, and yet he did nothing to stop Nellie. This wasn't the first time he had seen Nellie barter. When they first met, she named a price, and he had paid. There were others, too. Always others.

Julius's apartment was a dim cave, boxes and bulging green garbage bags littered the floor. "It's time to get my get on," he had said. "I'm moving 'cross town, down near the 'Fax and Five Points, the po-po station." Julius spat on his floor. "You staying safe out there?" he said. GI said that tempers were as high as the heat. The shelters were overrun, but GI didn't mention that Nellie refused to stand in line at the shelters. "Everyone's afraid of waking up dead," he said. Julius had laughed, his mouth opened, revealing two rows of silver-capped molars that flashed like miniature chainsaw blades. "I wake up dead, nearly every day," Julius said. "That's what gives me my pleasant disposition."

Around midnight, when they made to leave, Julius winked at Nellie and said that they could sleep on the floor. GI hefted his bag. Nellie said, "Might as well." Julius wiped his tongue across his front teeth. GI set his bag on the floor, the air-conditioning hissing a wicked coldness, and Nellie followed Julius to his bedroom. They unrolled their sleeping bags and listened as the bedsprings in the other room croaked a broken rhythm. Julius grunted, and GI lit a cigarette. He pictured himself sticking a knife in Julius, slicing him like the pig that he was. Finally, the springs stopped. GI closed his eyes, and, without opening them, he knew Nellie was next to him. He opened his eyes, and he and Nellie looked like nothing more than shadows existing in a single dimension—no depth, no time. She smelled sour and salty. She touched him, and the dimensions returned. Her skin was damp, and when she spoke he was surprised that she was not out of breath. Did she even live in her own body? She whispered, "I want my boy back."

Nellie's boy, Tommy, lived with a foster family in South Dakota or maybe Georgia. At the Fort Golan hospital they had given Nellie the juice so many times that her memories leaked right through, spilling behind her. Chico didn't believe that Tommy existed at all, but GI understood—he had three teenagers that he hadn't seen in ten years. He believed. He knew Nellie's pain, the anguish of lack, and he wanted to give her something more. He wanted to get up enough money to go to Key West, where he pictured Nellie sunbathing—she was the only homeless woman he had ever seen sunbathe!—and they would spare-change the tourists and sleep on the beach. No heat waves, no murders, no young homeless kids who prowled the streets like rabid dogs.

Nellie looked innocent in the sun. When she went to Julius, he could have said *No*. At Julius's, she had reached into GI's sleeping bag and pulled out his hand, kissed it, held it to her damp cheek. GI watched her and prayed: *Lord, be gracious to us. Thank you, Lord, for these few drops of whiskey we share. Thank you for letting us wake alive. Keep us safe from the things that want to destroy us.* He quietly prayed her name. *Nellie*. He said her name until he was dreaming Key West, and they swam in the ocean and kissed salty kisses. *Nellie.*

❖❖❖

In front of Denver Drug & Liquor, they waited for Ted. Nellie insisted on crossing the street, and GI tried to get her to wait. A zit-faced kid with a BMX bike and Chico exchanged words, and GI reached for Nellie as she stepped from the curb. Suddenly, the kid lifted the BMX bike and slammed it into Chico's upper body, and just as quickly, the kid was on the bike, across the street, and down the block before the first drop of blood hit the sidewalk. In the confusion, Ted and Nellie headed toward the river, and GI tended to Chico, who was dazed but still standing. GI looked around, waiting for the kid to return, but it was the cops that smelled the blood.

He sat in the back of the squad car, a free ride to detox, which, for the officer, meant less paperwork than a public drunkenness ticket. He knew the squad car well, number 723, his former brother-in-law, officer Victor Codaz. Victor drove slowly, and he met GI's eyes in the rearview. "You ever think about what it'll be like to burn in hell, Stuart?"

"Every single day."

"You'll be judged, you know. You were married in the eyes of God and had three children."

"I don't need your Jesus lectures. Heard 'em all before." Victor slammed on the brakes and quickly accelerated, throwing GI forward and then back, his weight slamming his cuffed wrists into the fiberglass seat.

"You could use an eternity worth of Jesus lectures."

"I know the story. He suffered to get you off scot-free. I don't need no one to suffer publicly for me. I suffer public near every day." The squad car passed the entryway to the detox center, which looked like a fortified emergency room entrance. "I'm not proud of what I done," GI said. "I've asked for Janice's forgiveness." Victor drove down Thirteenth, west, turned south and then west again on Highway 6, out of Denver County and into Jefferson County, pulling off at the Fairgrounds exit. GI remained silent. They stopped in a secluded pull-off. GI looked at the mountains—Lakewood right there, where Janice and the kids lived. It had been some time since he had been so close.

Victor got out of the car and opened the back door, where GI sat, silent, hands cuffed behind his back. Victor grabbed GI's arm and spun him around against the car. "Your suffering, Stuart, is not the suffering of

Christ. It's neglect." Pressing his elbow against GI's cheek, Victor stuck his hand into GI's pocket, pulled out two dollar bills, a few quarters and nickels. These Victor put in his own pocket. "I found a man last week, dead, leg sawed right off. His face was in the dirt, and I was hoping it was you."

"I suppose that's natural," GI said. Victor yanked on GI's hands, which remained cuffed behind his back. GI stood on his tiptoes, but the pain screamed through his wrists and shoulders. In one quick motion, Victor released the cuffs and GI's hands went slack against his sides. "The eight-mile walk will do you good," Victor said. "Must be over a hundred today."

GI stood with his arms at his side, watching as the squad car drove away. He began to walk. He was no stranger to walking. It would be dark by the time he got back. Nellie and Ted would have settled in somewhere. They had been moving about a lot recently, and some nights Ted and Chico opted to stay in the shelters, but not Nellie. Not him either. GI began moved his legs forward, step after step. Eight miles of steps before he reached Denver, more before he found Nellie.

Nellie slept under the bridge, slept like a dead person. Chico and Ted had left to get lunch at the shelter. GI was hungry, but Nellie made fun of the folks standing in the lines—food lines, bed lines, water lines—and now GI was too embarrassed to wait for anything.

Two days before, Jimmy Aces was found dead. Jimmy was a former blackjack dealer in Vegas, a man fond of showing off his tricks, and in death his cards had been spread around him; a bloody queen of hearts had been attached to his forehead. The day before, a homeless woman had been raped before she was killed. The cops found a dead black kid that morning. Rumors and theories were exchanged—turf wars between the old boys and the young dicks, the Freight Train Riders of America, the cops. Nellie had no theories about the murders. "Who hasn't been destroyed before?" she said. GI now carried a screwdriver in his pocket. Recently, he had traded some of his tools—tape measure, level, and chisel—for a Bowie knife.

Nellie was awake now, rubbing sleep from her eyes. "You need to take a sign to the street," Nellie said. He said that he didn't want to leave her alone. Under her breath, she mimicked him, and his face went flush. "I don't need anybody to look after me." Nellie stood at her cart, sorting clothing, looking at scraps of paper.

"If you don't need nobody to look after you, why do you need *me* to hold a sign?"

A helicopter circled overhead and Nellie swatted at it, as if it were a mud wasp approaching her hair. "Fucksake." She stood up and lifted her arms to the sky. "If you going to follow me all the time, you might as well make some use of yourself." She picked through her shopping cart, lifting blankets, clothes, undergarments. A boom box.

"Why not come with me?" GI said.

"Quit with your look, like you don't know if you want to fuck me or set me on your knee. And quit talking to every man like you *own* me or know what's best for me."

GI pulled a cardboard sign from his pack. Years ago, he told people that he was the first to put *veteran* on his cardboard signs, and they had called him GI ever since. He never said Vietnam, but people assumed just the same.

"I was out here long before I met you, making my way in good times and bad." She claimed to receive disability checks, but he never saw her go to a post office box. Nellie squatted in the bushes, her shorts and panties around her ankles. How many other men had stood before her while she pissed? She lacked modesty. She was vain. He wished he had the will to turn his head. Hiking up her shorts, Nellie stuck out her tongue. "I'd be happy, GI, if you would just go hold the sign for a party tonight." She cupped his chin in her hand. "Don't look so upset."

"What if we left, Nellie? Me and you." She stepped back, her eyes fearful. She had once told him that the electro-convulsion therapy stopped her from committing suicide. "Key West, Florida, Nellie. That's what I'm thinking."

"You can't even get us money for a bottle. How you going to get us to Florida?"

"You're wrong, Nellie. I can get us there." Ducks floated north on the Platte, and it occurred to GI that that was the wrong direction for a river to flow.

Nellie laughed. "Look at the rooster," she said. She pointed to GI and turned her head to look at the ducks floating by. "He's got his gander up, he does." She laughed, but the corners of her mouth were down again. "I'll go if you get us there," she said.

❖❖❖

GI returned from holding the sign, and Nellie's cart remained hidden behind a scrubby bush, his backpack wedged in beside it. She was nowhere to be seen. He held two bottles of beer, two cheeseburgers, a bag of fries, and a Baby Ruth bar, Nellie's favorite. Holding the sign had been hot work, the standing, the asphalt, the cars and buses. GI's skin felt like one giant blister ready to burst. He wanted to drink down one of the beers, or better, both beers, but he waited for Nellie. He pulled his sleeping bag from his pack and pushed it up against the bridge wall. She'd be back in a minute, and they'd have a little party, fight off the heat with a summer celebration. As he fell asleep, he imagined the smile she would give him when she saw the Baby Ruth bar.

As he often did after holding the sign, he dreamed of two girls and one boy looking out the back window of a station wagon, waving, sticking out their tongues. In the dreamscape, he initially felt hope after seeing the kids, but then fear and confusion set in. In the dream, he was never convinced that he would recognize his own children. They would not recognize him. GI woke from his dream, sweating as if bleeding the dream's sadness. A dry wind blew over the riverbed and paper rattled. He looked toward the sound, thinking schools and notebooks, and saw Nellie's shopping cart, the bottom lined with newspaper. "Nellie?" he said. No answer. He waited and listened. Their rules had been clear about keeping track of each other at night. "Nellie!" His voice cracked. She wasn't near. He heard someone laugh just up stream. "Hey," GI said, "You see anyone by the name of Nellie?"

"Don't know anyone named Nellie, so I might and I might not," was the answer that came back. GI rolled up his sleeping bag. Fishing through his pack, he pulled out the two beers and stuffed the sleeping bag inside the pack. He drank from one of the beers and tried to think, but he only saw the front-page newspaper pictures—bodies bagged and caught in a web of police tape.

"Nellie!"

GI took a notebook and pen from the pack.

Nellie,

I don't know were you went. You was on my ass to hold up the dam sine so I did and then your gone. I'm leving this note in cas you come back. How was I to know were the hell you went to?? I jus wish you wernt pissed. I don't know if you will read this. Wait for me if you fine this.

GI

A. K. A. Lawrence Saul Stuart Sr.

GI taped the note to the tree next to the shopping cart. He threw the pack on the shopping cart and headed down to the trail.

❖❖❖

Chico stood on South Santa Fe Drive holding a sign, and just below him, GI and Ted sat next to the Platte River in the shade, smoking and watching the river slowly move north. "I think you ask him," Ted said. "Sometimes those we least expect will show kindness." GI grunted. He leaned on Nellie's cart. He threw a pebble into the water and watched it vanish. "It wouldn't hurt is all I'm saying," Ted said.

"It *would* hurt," GI said. Traffic flowed from both Santa Fe and the Valley Highway, I-25. GI had been searching for Nellie almost non-stop for a week now. Chico said that hanging signs was a waste of time, but Ted said that signs worked for missing dogs and cats, why shouldn't it work for a missing woman? GI had checked with the police and at Fort Golan, but these were both a dead end. He didn't know Nellie's last name. Searching through the cart had turned up nothing. He wondered if her name was really Nellie. There was no ID in the cart, and there were no check stubs. Without any identification, she couldn't cash any checks. He hadn't let the cart out of his sight, not since she disappeared. Even at night, he kept his hand touching its black plastic wheel. When he found her, she would thank him for keeping such good care of all her things, all her possessions—her pictures of Tommy, her lady things, her winter clothes, her magazines.

GI stood at Nellie's cart. He felt guilty picking through her things like he had, but it had been necessary. He peeled the blanket back and folded it. A black bikini sat on top, and he ran his hand over the shiny fabric. On the bikini top GI saw what looked to be a fleck of skin. He pinched the skin between his thumb and finger and placed it on his tongue. He imagined the skin expanding, the dry cells filling with his saliva, Nellie growing inside of him. He would carry her and nurture her; his mouth would grow like a woman's belly, and after a time, she would emerge—Nellie would walk from his mouth. She would smile. She would curse him the way she liked to. Nellie would hold GI against her body, Nellie's body that had grown inside his body. GI and Nellie would hold each other next to the Platte River, and they would not know who was the mother, who was the child, or who were the lovers.

❖❖❖

GI pushed Nellie's cart, and for a moment the rattle of its stainless steel and rubber wheels was inaudible. Construction surrounded them—cranes, bulldozers, jackhammers—the sounds of progress. The old Forney Transportation Museum was wrapped in chain-link. They were building a new sporting goods store, a flagship store. GI remembered how when his children were small, he and Janice had taken them to the Forney Museum. GI guessed that the building was almost 100,000 square feet. Their tour guide was a bearded man with a gimp arm, and as they went through the museum, stuffed full of antique cars, planes, and trains, Janice had said she was creeped-out. Cobwebs hung over everything, and manikins were crudely clothed in the period of the vehicles they surrounded. The cars did not shine, the motorcycles did not seem fast—the entire museum was like a haunted house, and they had joked that the museum would make an excellent location for a *Dirty Harry* chase scene. Still, Janice was disturbed by the place. Now, walking away from the building, GI felt like he belonged inside of it, back in the past among the dusty and ill-positioned manikins, the rusted engines, and tattered upholstery. No one cared about that past; they hadn't cared when it was in disrepair, and they didn't care now that it would only be a memory. GI felt like a relic, one without value. An underdog object.

The boys kept walking, the skyscrapers of downtown off to their left. They approached Colfax. Officer Victor Codaz was parked in a lot next to Colfax and Speer. He ate a sandwich and appeared to be watching the traffic. He smiled when the three men approached. He stepped from his vehicle and placed his cap on his head.

"I need your help, Victor. I wouldn't be asking if I wasn't desperate." Victor looked equal parts entertained and bored. "I wouldn't ask you for a thing. Not ever. I know you don't like me." GI listened to the traffic grunt and halt, sigh and start. A helicopter flew overhead, moving slowly across the sky, as if a toy in the hands of some child, who at any moment, would play havoc on this toy city of buildings, dirt, and plastic people. "It's Nellie. She's been gone for weeks."

"Your woman?"

"I don't know her last name, Victor." GI's voice cracked. "I've searched everywhere and talked to just about everyone I thought could help."

Victor smiled. He nodded and rubbed his jaw. He looked beyond the men and into the dense city landscape rising beyond Speer. "I haven't spoken with her."

"But you've seen her?" GI's voice sounded like a child's filled with wonder and awe and want. "Would you tell me where, Victor?"

"It's only speculation, Stuart. I don't want to get your hopes up. What you really need to do is file an MPR."

"I've tried, but I don't know her last name," GI whispered.

"I heard she got picked up and taken to Golan." GI exhaled. He dug a cigarette from his pocket, lit it. The clouds moved from his vision, receding to the edges of his sight. "And then I think I saw her with Julius Krzycki."

"I thought she might be dead," GI said.

"I've talked to Julius," Chico said, "and he don't know where she is."

"Like I said, I *think* I saw her with Krzycki. Once or twice on Colfax. Late one night, Krzycki helped her get into a car. My guess is he's pimping her."

"I talked to him two days ago," Chico said. "He hadn't seen her."

Victor raised his hands in the air. "That's all I can tell you." The radio barked from his squad car. "If you'll excuse me." Victor walked to the car, stopped, and turned around. "I took her to Golan myself, Stuart. And you can best believe that if she was dead, I would find you and tell you. You have my word."

"You ain't even human," Ted said. He put his arm around GI.

"It ain't what you think, GI," Chico said. "He ain't pimping her out. Julius ain't a pimp, and Nellie ain't a Colfax girl."

GI braced himself against the shopping cart, as if it were a walker. She could still be at Fort Golan, but then again, the people at Golan said that it didn't matter what her last name was; they had no woman of Nellie's description. If she had left, she could be anywhere, somewhere out in Denver, looking for GI. *She was alive.* Nellie, her sweet body. Nellie, her stern voice. Nellie was out there. GI was convinced. He looked beyond the steep banks of the Platte, the beautiful, stupid, backward river, and he smiled for the first time since she had turned up missing.

On an embankment just behind the Six Flags amusement park, GI had Nellie's and his possessions spread out on the concrete. He scratched his head and did some quick math, and while some things he immediately knew the price of, others he needed to guesstimate. Charcoal $5—it said so right on the bag. He scratched down $14.00 for the small barbeque grill.

The tools were worth more than anything, with the exception of Nellie's lady stuff. $75.00. The two backpacks ten apiece; black markers, $6.00. Cooler $15.00. Two twenty-four-ounce beers inside the cooler $2.35. And how to price Nellie's lady stuff?—bras and underwear of different sizes and materials, wigs, dresses, a couple of bathing suits, and make-up in tubes, canisters, and compacts. GI's head spun. $200 was the best he could guess. And then there was other shit, random clothing, shoes, things, and more things. $100, maybe. All totaled it was nearly $400 in merchandise.

People ran stalls at the Mile High Flea Mart, but they gave bottom dollar on anything. He could pawn the tools. Nellie would be pissed if he sold her things, but he wasn't even sure where Nellie was, *if she was*, but, if she was, and he found her, they could get the hell out of Denver, maybe they could rent a place, and he could work where they wouldn't garnish child support. GI and Nellie would go to Key West, Florida, or New Orleans, Louisiana, anywhere but Denver, Colorado.

❖❖❖

Although it was over one hundred degrees, Julius wore a two-piece suit—a stained, white tank top beneath the jacket. He was working the streets early today. Julius scratched at the black growth on his face and nodded. "I don't know if I can help." Julius looked to the sky, kicked at a cigarette butt sitting at his tennis shoes. He offered GI a cigarette, and GI quickly took it. Julius smiled. "You know in my line a work, I can't just go telling a John where a girl is—even if she ain't mine. People have ulterior motives."

GI lifted the shopping cart and slammed it down. "She ain't no whore."

With a toothpick, Julius dug at his fingernails. "Where you been?"

"I'm telling you." GI shook his dirty finger at Julius. Julius laughed. "I'll fucking break you," GI said. He poked Julius's chest. Julius grabbed the finger and twisted it hard, the knuckles popped and folded. "Sonofabitch," GI said through gritted teeth. Julius twisted again. A sound came from Julius's mouth, a guttural pig's squeal. GI cried out in pain and fell to the ground. His forehead rolled against the pavement, and he inched himself toward the shopping cart. Looking up, he saw Julius's dirty tennis shoe, the creased pant legs, and the smiling face and silver-capped teeth.

"Stupid, stupid, stupid," Julius said. He placed his tennis shoe on GI's shoulder and gently rolled GI's shoulder back and forth. GI crawled toward the shopping cart; he reached for it with his left hand. Julius's foot came down on GI's arm, and putting his full weight forward, Julius reached into his back pocket. "You are one sorry piece of shit, always have been. Everything you touch turns to shit, but I guess it's because you are shit." GI stood, cradled the broken finger, and stepped toward Julius. "Quit while you're ahead," Julius said. He opened his jacket, a sheathed knife tucked inside his waistband.

"But when you run into Nellie." Julius unzipped his red trousers and pulled out his cock. GI looked away. "Hey, garbage man, when you run into Nellie, you let her know she can get her stuff back. All she's got to do is wrap her lips around this." Julius tucked himself back inside his red pants. "I bet you never even seen her dressed in any of this, GI." Julius held up a black bra and underwear. He dug through the clothes with one hand and pushed the cart with the other. He walked north toward Speer; the cart sounded a steady metal rattle. "See ya around. Here." Julius tossed a roll of duct tape at GI. "Fix that fucking finger, looks like you had it up your ass."

GI bent down and picked up the tape. A pigeon approached, its neck a series of hinges, opening and closing, its eyes two small, green jewels waiting to be plucked.

❖❖❖

GI felt broken and naked. The pain was lessened by a few hits off a bottle some generous soul had offered him. Initially, his finger looked like a short snake in an S-pattern, but as it swelled, it looked more like an over-boiled hot dog; meat zigzagged as it broke from the skin. He bought two flasks of whiskey, which he stuffed in his pants and covered with his shirt. The idea was to drink alone. When he began the descent to the bridge at Colfax over the Platte, he saw her. She was muttering to herself, but she looked sober and well fed. She laughed when she saw him, but then as he continued climbing down, she began to frantically look around the rest of the area underneath the bridge. Standing, she scanned the concrete under-side, the grass on the embankments, and even the bridge rafters. When GI was ten feet away from her, he said her name. *Nellie.*

"GI."

"Some people thought you might be dead."

"I ain't."

"I see that." Pigeon shit fell from the rafters. They both raised their eyes to the birds and the mound of white and black shit piling on the sill of the rafter. "I didn't like that you were gone without any word. We need to look out for each other, Nellie."

"Did you look after my stuff?"

GI pulled a bottle from his pants. "I did, Nellie. I had your cart with me the whole time." He paused, tried to decide: truth or lie. "I had it all the whole time. I swear."

"Fucking cops. There was no reason for it. Where's my cart?"

"Julius."

"Why in hell would Julius have my shit?"

"Look at my finger." GI held his finger up in the air. It looked as crooked as the letters he drew in the love messages he had left for her.

"Fuck your finger!" Nellie stood and pushed GI in the shoulder. "He's got it all?"

"Nellie, I'll get the stuff back. I've got a plan for us, a plan for somewhere else." GI held his hand away from Nellie, and they both sat down on a piece of cardboard. GI searched the darkened underbelly of the bridge for something he recognized, some material thing he could pull to him, but there was only Nellie, who would refuse him if he tried to touch her. Two mallards floated by. A male and a female both interbred with other ducks, misfits. Amid piles of brown foam, the ducks floated into the reeds, dipped their heads into the polluted water, and drank. The bird's bellies were stained from the Platte and Cherry Creek Rivers. The birds never left Denver. Even in the winter, they could feast off the grass at the always-green golf courses, but they lived short lives as they absorbed the poisons that industry dumped into the rivers. They didn't know any better—a poisonous life was the only life they had ever known.

"Julius do that to your finger?" Nellie lightly poked at the crippled digit. GI flinched and awaited her touch again. She ran her fingers along GI's, from the fingernail, following the S-curve down to the base of his finger, touched his thumb, and held his wrist.

"It hurts worse than bad, Nell. I swear to Christ, I'll get everything back together for us. Everything and then we'll get the fuck out of here." Nellie pulled GI into her breast, and she rubbed his head. GI wet her shirt, saliva and tears, wet kisses. "I thought you were dead, Nell. I don't care about my finger."

❖❖❖

The hammer was heavy in GI's pocket. He had followed Julius for two late afternoons and early evenings—out of his apartment, down to the diner, and back where he'd pick up more weed. Julius had once taught GI to pick locks, and now GI entered Julius's locked apartment. He wanted a cigarette. There was a pack on the table. In the corner, next to a barstool and a stack of empty beer cans sat a garbage bag, a black bra hanging out of the bag, as if the intestine of a punctured stomach. GI walked over to the bag, opened it, and breathed in the smell of Nellie's lady things, of everything that Nellie owned. He closed the bag and winced in pain. Nellie had tied it up for him using the duct tape to secure his index finger to his middle finger.

All he had to do was heft the bag over his shoulder and walk out the door. He had seen Nellie's cart out in the alley. Leaving quickly had been the idea. When it came down to it, he was no match for Julius. Julius was younger, stronger, and meaner.

When GI heard footsteps on the porch, GI hid behind the door and slipped the claw hammer from his pocket. The door opened, and GI swung the hammer as hard as his bad finger would allow him. There was a loud crack, two low grunts—one from each of the men, and Julius fell to the ground. GI dropped the hammer, and it brushed his leg as it fell, leaving behind a wisp of blood and small pieces of tooth. He leaned down and pulled Julius's money clip from his pants, took every bill inside, and threw the wallet back on Julius's face. "Show you," he said. He grabbed the hammer and the garbage bag and was out the door.

GI would take the cart down to Nellie, convince her to move, and then head to the Greyhound station. She was down under the bridge at Colfax and Speer. All told it would take them an hour, maybe even less.

When GI opened the door, he saw Victor sitting in car 723. The bag was in GI's good hand, the hammer dangled from the broken one. He dropped the bag and switched the hammer to his other hand. Victor opened the door of the cruiser and smiled some awful smile. GI lifted the hammer and decided that he would destroy every goddamned unkind thing.

As Victor stepped toward GI, his gun now drawn, GI thought of Nellie. Though he knew she was still down beneath the bridge, he imagined her calling his name, as he had called hers when she was missing. He imagined her calling the three names he was given at birth—*Lawrence Saul Stuart*. He could see her standing on the bank of the creek with her hands to her mouth, and he swore that a sound, a sound that was like her voice hissing his name in prayer, dropped from the sky and landed in his ears, blanketing everything in darkness.

Ivanov Reyez/Leah

*And Laban said, It must not be so done
in our country, to give the younger before
the firstborn.*

Genesis 29: 26

In the morning
why did you ask, Where's Rachel?
An easier question when you're spent.
You didn't question where you were last night.
You didn't see beauty; you didn't know the law.
You loved what you felt.

You entered my tent with a punch of the flap;
you entered me with a slap of the darkness.
I didn't have to disguise myself:
I lay as open as the law.
A woman is a woman: enough said.
But a man is also a man,
and that's why you woke up a boy.

If your moans had been named Rachel,
would they have been any louder,
billowing the tent as they did,
billowing the world as we did?

Ivanov Reyez/Early Morning Coffee in Santa Fe

We could see the mountains from his garden table,
mountains smoky and lilac, mountains he could name
like parsing the wet petals of a lavender rose.

When he raised his cup to drink, a Costa Rican brew,
it was like lifting a mountain, a spiritual glance
into what lay beyond our meager efforts to exist.

What contained us? What did we contain?
We could grow as high as the ceilings in his house,
as majestic and heavy as the vigas that held them,
as rich and free as the scent that greeted us.

We could be the breeze through the yarrows, the rain
on every leaf, the laughter in every house across the way,
the strength and weakness in every hug and careful kiss.

We could be like lovers whose cups never emptied.
We could be the darkness staring through the window
at the fleshly light, the pink cactus bud after a shower,
or we could be pensive like horses not drinking.

Maria Bennett/The Loss of Mathematics

when in love
numbers abandon us

the weight
of what we can
and cannot hold
becomes immeasurable

we know
more than the calculus of tongues
can tell

and it no longer matters
which of your thousand selves
i touch in shadow
as my own face
changes
each time we meet

and we are so close
we must imagine
the distance
between us

Maria Bennett/In Night All Is Passage

in night all is passage
where we have ransacked
the libraries of angels
in our sleep
and i have plaited clocks
in my hair
for each missed moment

we dance
the waltz of the bruised rose
as stars offer
wordless consolation
and body reaches
for body
in this dream
we ferry
beyond
wanting

Nathaniel Doll/Alone with a Crowd

All the words I've ever wanted to say,
Floating on a page,
Speechless like a mute;
Eating your words for a lifetime
Leaves you pretty hungry.
You are what an insomniac
Gladly sleeps to dream about.
Feelings expressed mean infinitely
More than feelings repressed.
I wish I could be anything
You ever wanted,
Hidden under a shroud of familiarity.
I'm the invisible wind
You think you hear—
Twitch in your eye
That lets you know someone is thinking of you.
I'll be the hero for the pusillanimous,
Cursing the ones lucky enough to share your presence,
Fighting with nobody but myself.
A glance from you shuts down the brain;
Returning the favor implies
A look from someone behind me.
When your filled diary
Becomes a bottom for a box,
Will my name even find one page?
Being nice is the immeasurable end of desirability,
The beginning of getting to know yourself too well—
Impossible to complain, gripe, or cry,
A harlequin to the world am I.

Lara Gularte/Mushroom Woods

Evergreen forests
offer their leaves,
and below the surface of this world
mushrooms hide,
wait for the right moment.
A cold, dry season
then warm winds, rains
bring forth mycelium masses
that rise up to claim the forest floor.
In darkened thickets
where leaf mat covers ground
they thrust upward,
push through leaves and soil,
explode into moist clumps
to spread spores, seed-like hopes
of future species—
Red Russulas with chalk-white stripes
and spongy, brown *Boletus.*
Yellow globe of Witch's butter,
the faint lavender of blewits.
Slice a red-pored bolete
and its flesh turns blue.
There is risk in naming,
danger in misnaming,
and a short time
to hunt them
before the first frost.

Lara Gularte/What Might Take Her Back

When she leaves her life
filled with ritual and ruse,
the cool breath of the forest
opens up to her.

Ferns and brambles rise up
and great-winged birds.

Like a tree,
she remembers her story
of each ring,
years of flood and drought,
scarred skin.

In the woods
with no signposts
she walks in circles,
kicks at stones.
Time tastes gritty
in her mouth.

On the trail ahead
feathers lie strewn.
She ties her red scarf to a branch;
the wind blows it away.

From far away
her life comes back
like a thrown voice.

Bill Brown/The Little Blue Corporal

It's rare to see a Merlin on the ridge,
bigger than a kestrel, but not quite
a peregrine. Watch it hunt and you'll
learn how it earned that name. First,
identify the prey, then fly off slow,
not to affright it, then dart it,
that quick, that clean, sometimes
screaming ki-ki-ki, or byk-byk-byk.
Legend has Merlin born of woman,
sired by an incubus, that mysterious
immortal that seduces females
in their sleep. Some tales have
Merlin a wise wizard, others
a madman. In my short life
of spiritual groping, I used
to imagine a world in which
every creature that strove to be
its best would win another life
in higher form. I understand
this desire in a cockroach, aardvark
or human, but why would a Merlin
want to be anything else? Falconers
call the male The Little Blue Corporal
in its brown and slate blue uniform;
our desire, perhaps, to dress a creature
we admire in human garb. There he goes—
off the snag, winging low to the ground,
then a burst of speed, up and gone,
that clean, that quick.

Bill Brown/This Poem

We never signed up for this lottery—
tornados, lightning strikes, spider bites—
droughts, floods. We could easily blame the earth
for our sorrows. After being awake all night
listening to Storm Tracker watch twenty twisters
blister Tennessee, I take coffee to the porch
and find my trellis bright with morning glories.

For the infant buried in trailer rubble,
for the mill worker whose home was flattened,
for the CEO airlifted from the roof
of her drowned Mercedes,
    I write this poem.

For my worthless cats who hunt butterflies,
for my mother who waits for dead relatives to visit,
for the raccoons who wreck my bird feeders,
for my tomato plants red with fruit,
    I write this poem.

For the little brown bat that embraces darkness,
for the whippoorwills who lay their eggs
in the peril of the forest loam,
for the raucous crows who document death,
    I write this poem.

For the eye sockets of deer skulls,
for empty turtle shells,
for the hulls of cicadas,
for all of the bones and exoskeletons
that decorate this hallowed grave—
miraculous, terrible, lovely and unjust,
    I wake in the deepest part of night
    and write this poem.

I, whose bones will one day fold into ashes,
    fall to my knees
      and write this poem.

Larry Stein/Masks

CHARACTERS

MARK EDELSTEIN, *57: About 5'10 and balding. Has an average build. Wears a button down shirt.*

MICHELLE EDELSTEIN, *about 48: Wife of Mark. About 5' 7".*

BILL LOWE, *early 50s: Of Chinese ancestry. Neighbor of Mark and Michelle. About 5'9'.*

LISA LOWE, *late 40s: Wife of Bill. Also of Chinese ancestry. About 5'6". A high school teacher.*

ASSORTED CHILDREN

TWO TEENAGERS

SCENE

It is Halloween at dusk. A man in his mid-fifties wearing a button down shirt, casual slacks, a corduroy sport coat and a dog mask is sitting in a loveseat that is labeled "Loveseat." He has a Scotch in front of him. His wife is sitting across from him in a loveseat that is also so labeled. She is in her late forties wearing jeans and a Pasadena School of Design sweatshirt. She has a glass of diet Coke in front of her. She looks unhappy.

MICHELLE: Mark, please take off that ridiculous mask.

MARK: *(He takes off the dog mask and puts on a cat mask.)* You've seemed unhappy lately. I've decided you need a pet. Should it be a dog or cat?

MICHELLE: Since I quit drinking a lot of feelings have welled up.

MARK: *(Takes a sip of his Scotch.)* I used to drink Old Weller, a great bourbon. That makes me think of "Old Yeller." Perhaps, we should get a dog.

MICHELLE: I've felt angry.

(A doorbell rings. Mark goes to the door and opens it. There are three children dressed as witches.)

CHILDREN: Trick or treat?

MARK: Treat. *(He puts candy in each of their bags. He closes the door and starts back to the loveseat. He is now wearing the dog mask.)* Never a cauldron when you need one.

MICHELLE: I feel invisible. No one hears me.

MARK: Both dogs and cats have acute hearing. That will not be a deciding factor. I wish you would focus.

MICHELLE: I've been angry and am angry.

MARK: Your sister has been catty lately and your mother has been dogging you.

MICHELLE: Not funny. It's not them, it's. . .

(A doorbell rings. Mark goes to the door and opens it. There are two older children dressed as Chewbacca.)

CHILDREN: Trick or treat?

MARK: Treat. *(He puts candy in each of their bags. He closes the door and starts back to the loveseat. He is now wearing the cat mask.)* That would be quite a pet. By the way, I've invited Bill and Lisa to come by. They have a dog and a cat. They should be able to give us some insight.

MICHELLE: I don't think now's a good time.

MARK: I agree. I told them to come by in half an hour. Hopefully, by then, most of the trick or treaters will have started their sugar highs, and we can have a quiet chat.

MICHELLE: You're not listening to me.

MARK: Of course I'm listening. You're angry with your mother and sister. What else is new?

MICHELLE: Mark, you know I've always been there for you.

MARK: Not always.

MICHELLE: Just last year I helped you through chemotherapy, and just one year after our marriage, I nursed you and your brother back to health after your kidney transplant.

MARK: True, but you weren't there for my bypass surgery.

MICHELLE: You were married to your first wife then.

MARK: Well, speaking of Miriam, you weren't there when she died in the fire. That was a very difficult time for me.

MICHELLE: I didn't know you then.

MARK: Facts are facts. I wish you would quit switching the subject. A pet is a major commitment; we should take the time to discuss this.

MICHELLE: Let me try this a different way. You know Simon.

MARK: I know what Simon says. He says that you're quite talented and that he's enjoying collaborating with you. I know that you spend hours each day on line and on the phone working with him. He's quite famous. I think he may be able to open some doors for you.

MICHELLE: Well, Simon wants to live with me.

MARK: When I said open doors, I didn't necessarily mean ours. I think we should decide about our pet before we consider taking in boarders. *(The doorbell rings. Mark goes to the door and opens it.)* Hi, come on in. How are the two of you? You're a bit early.

LISA: Sorry, I hope it's no trouble. Our grandchildren are making our house their last stop. We need to get back by eight.

MARK: You know you and Bill are always welcome, but Michelle did want you here a little later.

MICHELLE: Mark's just kidding. It's great to see you both.

MARK: Have a seat. *(Lisa sits down next to Michelle and sets her purse beside her on the floor. Bill sits across from her. Mark walks towards the wet bar.)* What will you both have?

BILL: I will follow you into that Scotch bottle and Lisa will have the usual.

MARK: A double Scotch and a white wine coming up.

MICHELLE: So Bill, how is the world of physics? *(Mark heads towards Bill and Lisa and hands them their drinks. He sits next to Bill across from Michelle.)*

BILL: String theory has me tied up in knots. Actually things are going well. It's just we physicists don't have that many jokes.

MARK: Don't get me started on lawyer jokes. We have plenty. It's just that people are laughing at us, rather than with us. There must be some great big bang jokes. I bet your cat loves the string theory.

Bill: He's more into metaphysics. He wants to know how many mice can dance on the head of a pin.

MARK: I didn't know mice could dance.

LISA: Enough, you two. If I don't put a stop to this, it could go on forever. Michelle, how are you doing?

MICHELLE: Well, I quit drinking about a month ago, and I'm dealing with a lot of issues.

MARK: Like whether to get a dog or cat. *(Bill and Lisa exchange a glance)*

LISA: Does it bother you if we drink?

MICHELLE: Thanks for asking. No, it's fine.

MARK: *(Mark holds up his glass)* To warm nights and cool friends. *(Glasses clink; everyone takes a sip)*

(A doorbell rings. Mark goes to the door and opens it. There are two children, one with an Obama mask the other with a Sarah Palin mask.)

CHILDREN: Trick or treat?

MARK: Treat. *(He puts candy in each of their bags. He closes the door and starts back to the loveseat. He is still wearing the cat mask.)* It's great that we live in a mixed neighborhood. Republicans and Democrats living in perfect harmony.

BILL: Perhaps, all we need to do is give candy to Congress.

LISA: More treats, less tricks—good plan.

MARK: Lisa, you're the dog person. Give us the pros and cons.

LISA: Based on your mask, you've already decided.

MARK: *(He holds up the dog mask.)* No, I am truly impartial.

LISA: Well then, the advantage of a dog is unconditional love. Your dog will be as happy to see you the 500th time you come home as the first time. A dog is a pack animal. It requires attention and time. Leave a dog alone too much, it may become destructive. They just take more time and care. Dogs are creatures of habit. They like to be walked and fed at regular times. A dog will let you know if you're off its schedule.

MARK: And your thoughts, Bill?

BILL: Cats have the opposite advantages and disadvantages. Cats are more standoffish. You have to earn a cat's love and affection. Cats are not pack animals. They require less care. A cat can amuse itself and needs almost no attention if it has another cat to play with. You can leave out a supply of food for a cat. Unlike a dog it will not overeat. Being less domesticated they behave more like animals in the wild which makes them fun to watch. Kittens can have you laughing for hours.

MARK: Whether a cat or a dog, what about purebreds or mixed breeds?

BILL: As a scientist I believe in hybrid vigor. Plus with purebreds there's a chance you're supporting a puppy or kitten mill with bad conditions and excessive inbreeding.

MICHELLE: Lisa, you two have a cat and a dog. How have you made that work?

LISA: The usual. They have shared values and goals. They both worship the Prime Rib. Actually the secret is they grew up together. Bow thinks that Chasu's part of his pack.

(A doorbell rings. MARK goes to the door and opens it. He places candy in the bag of each of the pirates and goblins.)

MICHELLE: *(In a stage whisper, while Mark is at the door)* Lisa, I hate to be rude, but Mark and I have something we need to discuss.

MARK: I heard that, and it's true. We need to caucus on this pet issue. We will let you know the winner when all the results are in. Say hello to the grandchildren for us.

LISA: We'll see you soon.

(Mark and Michelle walk Bill and Lisa to the door. Goodbyes are exchanged. Mark closes the door and they return to their loveseats.)

MARK: This will be a difficult decision.

MICHELLE: Mark, that isn't what I want to talk about.

MARK: I know, but it's what I want to listen to.

MICHELLE: You can't keep hiding from reality.

MARK: Is there anything better to hide from? Now, hiding from fantasy, that would be my definition of insanity. If I were under the bed, afraid of Tinkerbell, you would certainly have grounds to complain.

MICHELLE: It's so difficult to talk with you.

MARK: Conversation is more an art than a science. As an artist, you know better than I that art is subjective and difficult. Although there is some art that's just plain bad. Dogs playing poker is bad. Even with the little bit I now know about dogs, I know it's impossible for them to bluff. They get too excited.

MICHELLE: Speaking of excited, have you ever had an affair?

MARK: I had a brief affair, but I went back to boxers. Boxers are good dogs, but so-so undergarments. It's just that I come from a boxer family. But I am a button down kind of guy. I like the control of briefs. I think I'm going to rise above my heritage with my bottoms. What about you?

MICHELLE: Mark, that's out of character even for you.

MARK: I get to decide what my character is. So do you prefer boxers or briefs?

MICHELLE: Let me be more specific. During our marriage have you ever had sex with another woman?

MARK: I will not give the Clintonian response.

(A doorbell rings. Mark goes to the door and opens it. There are four children, two dressed as angels and two as devils.)

CHILDREN: Trick or treat?

MARK: Treat. *(He puts candy in each of their bags. He closes the door and starts back to the loveseat. He is now wearing the dog mask.)* You know in the Jewish religion there's no other worldly heaven or hell. We make our own heaven or hell in this world.

MICHELLE: It will be pretty hellish if you don't answer my question.

MARK: That's a case in point. But let me answer. During our marriage I've never felt the passion for anyone that I've felt for you.

MICHELLE: Then, judging from your level of passion for me, you couldn't have had an affair.

MARK: Cruel logic is often the most incisive. Bravo on your powers of deduction.

MICHELLE: You know during our first year of marriage I found a condom in your pocket. You never explained that.

MARK: True.

MICHELLE: I let it slide, but I never forgot it. It's one of the things that has made me so insecure in our marriage.

MARK: Shouldn't it be out-secure? Insecure sounds like it means being in a state of security. English is a strange language.

(Michelle goes over to the wet bar grabs the bottle of Scotch and in frustration is about to throw it in the fireplace when the doorbell rings. Mark goes to the door and opens it)

MARK: Bill, what a pleasant surprise to see you again. Michelle must've had a premonition. She's getting the Scotch.

Bill: Sorry, Lisa left her purse. I can't stay long. I want to get back to the grandchildren. *(Bill goes to where Lisa was sitting and picks up her purse.)*

MICHELLE: Would you like a nightcap?

BILL: No, I have to get back.

MARK: Before you go let me ask you a question. Michelle and I are having a bit of a disagreement. I think it's about whether I should stick with boxers or switch to briefs. My position is that boxers and button down shirts do not go together. I don't mean visually. I'm not that demonstrative. I mean philosophically. I think Michelle likes the Superman/Clark Kent thing—mild mannered on the outside, but free and wild underneath. I have two problems with that. That's not me, and I'm a bit claustrophobic. I can't handle phone booths. Don't worry. I'm not going to ask you to weigh in on undergarments. But having an argument made me wonder what your and Lisa's secret is in sustaining a relationship for almost 25 years.

BILL: I have not quite come up with the Unified Field Theory of relationships, but I do have my three room hypothesis. For me, the living room represents communication, the most important part of a relationship. The bedroom is obvious, but communication is important there as well. The kitchen represents warmth and sustenance.

MICHELLE: Thanks, Bill. I had to get a word in before Mark made a bathroom joke. On a night of ghouls and goblins it's nice to have a touch of humanity.

MARK: She knows me too well.

BILL: I need to get back to the kids. See you guys soon.

(Bill exits through the front door carrying Lisa's purse. Mark and Michelle walk him to the door.)

MARK: See you soon. Give our love to your family. *(Mark and Michelle return to the loveseats.)*

MICHELLE: What did you think about what Bill said?

MARK: He likes small houses.

MICHELLE: Enough! Maybe I can get your attention by focusing on the bedroom. Between the cancer and the chemotherapy you lost almost one hundred pounds, much of it muscle.

MARK: And I didn't have much muscle to lose.

MICHELLE: I had feelings for you, and I still do, but it was like being with a child, not a romantic partner. I can't get that image out of my mind. For the past two years I've needed to get high to. . .

<hr />

(A doorbell rings. Mark goes to the door and opens it. There are two older children dressed as police.)

CHILDREN: Trick or treat?

MARK: Treat, if it's not a bribe. *(He puts candy in each of their bags. He closes the door and starts back to the loveseat. He is now wearing the dog mask.)*

MICHELLE: I've needed to get high to have sex with you.

MARK: I support your sobriety, but I didn't know that the third of the twelve steps is to quit sleeping with your husband. That explains why we haven't had sex since you quit drinking, and, really, not often in the past two years. I'd hoped to have a romantic evening before you left for Ireland for you and Simon to try to place works in Dublin galleries. I now feel very insecure about you being with the Celtic Tiger. We should see a marriage counselor.

MICHELLE: Perhaps, now you understand a bit of what it feels like to be insecure in our marriage. From very early on you made me feel that every woman you'd been with before me was somehow better or prettier. You put Miriam on a pedestal, and she treated you so much worse than I.

MARK: Statues are of the dead. Do you begrudge Miriam a bit of cold marble after the tragic life she lived and her even more tragic death? Pictures are of the living.In truth my first marriage was not a pretty picture. After her accident she lived fifteen years in a haze of pain and pills. I cared for her as best I could. I probably married you too soon after the fire. I thought I was all right, but I was probably deluding myself. I was still emotionally numb and wracked with guilt.

MICHELLE: You had no reason to feel guilt. Most men would have cut and run.

MARK: Maybe that's why I became a lawyer. I believe in the sanctity of contracts. I had hoped for better, but I'd promised to stay for worse. Plus, Miriam married me knowing I had kidney problems. I could hardly leave her when she had a health problem. But the main reason was she was so helpless. I didn't think she would survive without me.

MICHELLE: Maybe she would have gotten stronger without you. It sounds like a co-dependent relationship. Her problem may have been more addiction than illness. But why do you feel guilty?

MARK: *(Mark takes a deep drink)* My memory of the evening is still so vivid.

I got home from work to find fire engines, one police car, and reporters. I was told she'd died in a fire. She fell asleep in the recliner while smoking. Then the police questioned me to make sure I wasn't responsible. Reporters tried to get me to make a statement. I didn't. I don't know why people speak to reporters after personal tragedies. The firemen wouldn't let me back in the house. They asked me if they could get me anything from the house. I'd called Bill and Lisa and they offered to let me stay there. I was so crazy that I asked them to get a bottle of Scotch from the bar. A bottle of Scotch. Could I have come up with anything stupider to ask for? They brought me out a bottle of Midori. So I went to Bill and Lisa's with the clothes on my back, memories of Miriam and a bottle of Midori.

MICHELLE: Some of this I've heard before. But what is the cause for guilt?

MARK: I hate to answer a question with a question. But before I go on there are some things I need to know. I hear emotion better than I feel it or speak it. Is our marriage in jeopardy? I love you and would hate to lose you.

MICHELLE: Yes.

MARK: Flagellation without purpose is the worst form of self-indulgence. So before I beat myself up, I need to know if there's any hope for us working this out.

MICHELLE: I don't know. The drinking was covering a lot of anger and pain. Tell me about your guilt.

MARK: I felt grief for the loss of Miriam and for the life she could've and should've had but for her injury. But caring for her for fifteen years was difficult. Whenever she failed to answer the phone I was in a panic that something awful had happened. My fears were often justified. One evening she left to join a friend and after many frantic hours I got a call from Sybil Brand women's prison at three in the morning. She'd been incarcerated for driving under the influence. So when she died, there was a part of me that felt relieved. To feel relieved that your wife died a horrible death is a powerful source of guilt. But that isn't the worst. One thing that will haunt me forever is. . . *(A doorbell rings. Mark goes to the door and opens it. There are two teenagers without costumes or bags. They stick out their hands.)*

TEENAGERS: Trick or treat?

MARK: Treat. You look old enough to perform a serious trick. You have the scariest costumes of the night. *(He puts candy in their hands. He closes the door and starts back to the loveseat.)*

MICHELLE: So what is it that will haunt you forever?

MARK: One evening I came home and she'd fallen asleep in the recliner with a cigarette in her hand. It was the time I made her promise that when she was alone she would only smoke outdoors or in one of the bathrooms. A promise she obviously didn't keep. She was quite out of it from the Soma she must have taken. Opiates never were a problem. Like many people in chronic pain opiates made her seem normal, but Soma made her groggy and sort of punch drunk. When I confronted her she denied she was groggy or out of it. I was so frustrated. Before, when I had thrown the Soma down the toilet, she just got a doctor to write another prescription. Even when I got her into a treatment center they concentrated on the opiates but she convinced them to let her have the Soma. So I just wanted her to admit the effect it was having on her. I got the awful idea of slapping her to show her how slow her reflexes were—that she couldn't block my hands.

MICHELLE: Well, your frustration was understandable.

MARK: Perhaps, but you have to understand the situation. My guilt isn't from physically hurting her. I barely tapped her. It's not because of the one, and only time, I've struck a woman. It was the look of betrayal on her face. Her mother had abused her, and her father, whom she idolized, had already passed. Pills and pain had cut her off from friends and family. I was her last lifeline. She had the look of a helpless child. There was such a look of loss in her face. I still see that face in my dreams. So that pedestal was built out of guilt. But fear not, the pigeons will find the statue soon enough.

MICHELLE: You know I sympathize for you and your loss. But you devoted so much time and effort to Miriam. I've never felt you cared for me the same way. You often pushed me away. I've felt distant from you. When you were away I often cried. I think that's why I started drinking heavily.

MARK: You were so functional I never realized how much you were drinking. But I see the difference now. You and Simon are really cranking it out.

MICHELLE: Thanks. But I want to know what happened? You were so attentive and passionate when we met. But it wasn't long before I was wondering why you married me. You seemed to think of me as a boring *hausfrau*. I lost all my confidence.

MARK: I have always found you beautiful and exciting. But I was so lonely. I fell in love too quickly. Once the initial excitement wore off, I think guilt took hold. I wanted to make you happy, but I think I've sabotaged our relationship.

MICHELLE: And, what's this thing about getting a pet?

MARK: I know you wanted to have a child. But it didn't work out. Although we never saw a fertility doctor, I think my sperm had trouble swimming upstream. In fact, I'm not sure they could swim. A drowning sperm isn't very appealing to an egg. I thought maybe a pet would help fill the gap.

MICHELLE: Well, that's the root of our problem. You decide what I need. You never ask me what I want, or if you do, you ignore my answer.

MARK: What do you mean?

MICHELLE: Let me give you a simple example. You will ask me where I want to eat and if I answer you come up with another option. I just give up and do what you want to do. It's the story of our marriage.

MARK: You so seldom object or tell me what you want. I don't know what to do to make you happy. Then there are those times when you explode. I don't handle conflict well, so I just try to calm things down. Would you like to go to a fertility doctor, or consider adopting again?

MICHELLE: I didn't want to go to a fertility doctor or to adopt before. I certainly don't want to do either now.

MARK: Why didn't you want to adopt or see a specialist?

MICHELLE: In part I wanted to get my career going. But maybe I wasn't ready to quit drinking.

MARK: *(Mark gets up and heads towards the doorway to the office and bedroom)* I'm going to get my laptop. You have to see the dogs and cats on the Glendale Humane Society website. They're so cute. I'm sure you'll see the perfect one for us.

MICHELLE: You're not hearing me. I don't know if there is an "us." I'm not willing to make a commitment with you, be it a child or a pet.

MARK: Well, looking on the bright side, if we're not going to adopt a child or rescue an animal, we can both get two-seat sports cars. We've no need for backseats.

MICHELLE: You can't distract me that easily. Storm clouds don't have silver linings.

MARK: What about marriage counseling?

MICHELLE: I don't know. During my years of alcohol haze, I may've fallen out of love with you. It may be too late.

MARK: *(Looking despondent)* Is there anything I can say or do? *(Mark heads to the wet bar carrying his glass and pours himself some Scotch)* Can I get you some more diet Coke?

MICHELLE: That's another thing. You don't respect my sobriety. You're constantly drinking in front of me.

MARK: I've asked you if it was all right. You said yes. When I started to move bottles from the liquor cabinet to the basement you said I was being condescending. I thought I was just descending. I feel like if you asked me to shoot my foot, and I did, you'd tell me I shot the wrong one.

MICHELLE: I shouldn't have to tell you about drinking. You should know what to do.

MARK: Words have meaning. When I draft a contract the parties can look at it ten years later, and because of the precision of the words, know their obligations. If I draft properly no litigation will cast asunder the business union I helped to create. I'm not good at guessing or subtext. But I'm proud of you.

MICHELLE: You never really answered me about the condom.

MARK: I would prefer not to. It's something that I'm ashamed of.

MICHELLE: On this night of masks yours must come off.

MARK: *(Mark gets up and paces)* I was getting lap dances at strip clubs. That's what the condom was for.

MICHELLE: Do you know how that makes me feel?

MARK: That's why I didn't want to tell you.

MICHELLE: Until recently I was always a willing partner. Aren't I pretty enough?

MARK: Of course you are. That's not it.

MICHELLE: Well, what is it then?

MARK: I guess there's some appeal to excitement without emotions or expectations. But really I think it's just a bad habit.

MICHELLE: How long has this been going on?

MARK: It really goes back to Miriam. For the last fifteen years of our marriage we seldom made love. There were a lot of reasons. Her neck and back problems made me afraid of hurting her. Also the steroids and anti-depressants the doctors gave her caused her weight to balloon up. But the main reason is that our relationship became more of a parent/child than a husband and wife relationship. That may sound familiar. To me commercial sex was much better than having an affair because it did not involve love or emotion.

MICHELLE: But why did you continue after you met me? I feel betrayed.

MARK: I guess it became a habit, or addiction. My visits tapered off quite a bit after I met you.

MICHELLE: But didn't stop.

MARK: No. But I'll stop. You've stopped drinking. I certainly can do this.

MICHELLE: I just feel that you have cheated in our marriage. I feel you have not respected me.

MARK: I'm so sorry. But is cheating about orgasm or emotions? I believe Simon is more of a threat to our marriage than a few lap dances.

MICHELLE: Your detachment has been the problem. The failure of our marriage isn't based on Simon. He's the result of that failure. I should let you know that my ticket to Dublin is one way.

MARK: I guess it's too much to hope for that it's from Dublin to Los Angeles. Well then, I guess I'll get a dog. I'm too old, tired and depressed to earn love. *(Mark gets up and heads towards the doorway to the office)* I guess I should start researching dog foods. *(The lights dim except for a spotlight on Mark's face. He takes off the dog mask and underneath is a tear-stained human mask. There is a pause, and then there is the sound of one person clapping. The lights come up and Michelle is standing and lightly clapping.)*

MICHELLE: That mask was a nice touch.

MARK: Thanks.

MICHELLE: Do you want to try breaking up with me tomorrow?

MARK: Sure. Who shall we invite over?

MICHELLE: How about Charles and Christopher?

MARK: What will the topic *du jour* be?

MICHELLE: Thanksgiving is almost here, and they're both foodies. How about whether to have a traditional or smoked turkey?

MARK: That sounds perfect.

MICHELLE: I hope we decide to have both.

MARK: You're the best. *(He takes her hand and they walk towards the wet bar)* Let's get a bottle of champagne and go to bed. It's time for our own tricks and treats. *(Hand in hand with a bottle of champagne they head towards the door to the office and bedroom. The lights fade.)*

CONTRIBUTORS NOTES

Sandy Aragon is a creative writing student at Glendale College who was born in Hidalgo, Mexico. She is the first in her family to attend college. Her goal is to transfer to USC, majoring in Accounting and Business Administration.

Azatuhi Babayan, a former creative writing student at Glendale College, is now a junior at Cal Berkeley, studying literature and reveling in the lush scenery of the Bay Area. She hopes to travel through Scandinavia someday to satiate her wanderlust and drag a certain Icelandic post-rock band out of hiding.

Maria Bennett teaches creative writing at Hostos Community College of the City University of New York, where she has been an Assistant Professor of English for twenty-seven years. Her original work and her translations of the poets Nancy Morejon, Ernesto Cardenal, and Cintio Vitier have appeared in *Nexus, Crab Creek Review*, and *Esprit* magazines.

Bill Brown teaches part-time at Vanderbilt University. He has authored four poetry collections, three chapbooks and a textbook. His two current collections are *Late Winter* (Iris Press, 2008) and *Tatters* (March Street Press, 2007). Recent work appears in *Prairie Schooner, Tar River Poetry, English Journal, Southern Poetry Review*, and *Connecticut Review*.

Elena Karina Byrne is the Poetry Consultant/Moderator for *The Los Angeles Times* Festival of Books, reviewer for ForWord's Clarion Reviews, and Literary Programs Director for The Ruskin Art Club. Her publications include *2009 Pushcart Prize XXXIII Best of the Small Presses, Best American Poetry 2005, The Yale Review, The Paris Review, APR, The Kenyon Review, Ploughshares, Poetry,* and *TriQuarterly.* Books include: *The Flammable*

Bird, (Zoo Press/Tupelo Press, 2002); *MASQUE* (Tupelo Press, 2008) and the forthcoming *Burnt Violin* (Tupelo Press, 2011).

Ashley M. Carrasco is a creative writing student at Glendale College who was born and raised in the heart of Los Angeles. She graduated from UCSD and is currently pursuing a career in media.

R.T. Castleberry is a widely published poet and social critic. He was a co-founder of the Flying Dutchman Writers Troupe and co-editor/publisher of the monthly magazine *Curbside Review*. His chapbook, *Arriving At The Riverside*, was published by Finishing Line Press in 2010.

Tom Chandler is poet laureate of Rhode Island emeritus. He has been named Phi Beta Kappa Poet at Brown University and has been a featured poet at the Robert Frost homestead. He is a columnist for *The Providence Journal*, a professor of creative writing at Bryant University, and the founder and editor of the *Bryant Literary Review*. His latest book of poems is *Toy Firing Squad*.

Ginny Lowe Connors is the author of the poetry collection *Barbarians in the Kitchen* and has edited three poetry anthologies, including *Proposing on the Brooklyn Bridge* and *Essential Love*. She works as an English teacher in West Hartford, Connecticut.

Nick Conrad's poetry has appeared in recent or forthcoming issues of *Borderlands, Common Ground Review, The Dos Passos Review, Edison Literary Review, Front Range, J Journal, the Kerf, The Mochila Review, The Portland Review, South Carolina Review, Southern Poetry Review, Stand* (UK), *Talking River, Texas Literary Review*, and *Wisconsin Review*.

Jim Daniels' latest book of poems, *Having a Little Talk with Capital P Poetry*, was published by Carnegie Mellon University Press in 2011. *From*

Milltown to Malltown, a collaborative book with photographer Charlee Brodsky and writer Jane McCafferty, was published in 2010 by Marick Press.

John Davis lives on an island in Puget Sound, Washington. His poems have appeared recently or are forthcoming in *New York Quarterly, The North American Review, Passages North and Poetry Northwest.* A chapbook, *The Reservist,* appears from Pudding House Press. A full collection, *Gigs,* is forthcoming from Sol Books.

Paul Diamond runs Casagrande Press, a small publisher of fiction and nonfiction books. He's taught writing at Ohio University and Tulane University. He grew up in Washington D.C. and now lives in Seattle where, for a living, he writes and manages content for a corporation you would not care to know about.

Nathaniel Doll is a creative writing student at Glendale College who grew up in Saint Clair Shores, Michigan and moved to Glendale with the hopes of making it as a screenwriter.

Will Dowd is currently pursuing an MFA at New York University. His work has appeared in *Post Road Magazine, 32 Poems, The Comstock Review,* and is forthcoming in *Flatmancrooked's Slim Anthology of Contemporary Poetics.*

James Doyle's most recent poetry book, *Bending Under the Yellow Police Tapes,* was published by Steel Toe Books in 2007. He has poems forthcoming in *Alaska Quarterly Review, Seneca Review, Margie, Beloit Poetry Journal, Pearl,* and *Poet Lore.* He lives in Fort Collins, Colorado.

Anny Edinchikyan is a sophomore at Glendale Community College. She is a political science major who hopes to become a lawyer. This is her first publication.

Gail Rudd Entrekin teaches college level creative writing and English literature. Her most recent poetry collection is *Change (Will Do You Good)* (Poetic Matrix Press, 2005). She is Poetry Editor of Hip Pocket Press and the ezine *Canary*.

Toni Fuhrman is a novelist and short story writer who grew up in Ohio and has lived in Chicago, Cleveland, Detroit, and Ann Arbor, with sabbaticals in London, where she wrote her first novel, and India. She is now living and writing in Los Angeles.

Emily M. Green lives and writes in Oxford, Mississippi, where the sweet tea is so sweet it makes your teeth ache and the hospitality is as Southern as it gets. She holds an MFA in fiction from the University of Mississippi and another in poetry from the University of Wisconsin-Madison.

Robert Guard attended Ohio University. After graduation he became an advertising copywriter and worked in the marketing field. His poems have appeared or are forthcoming in *Argestes*, *The Chaffin Journal*, *descant*, *Nimrod*, *Quercus Review*, *Sycamore Review*, and *Harpur Palate*. He resides in Cincinnati.

Lara Gularte's poetry has appeared in such journals as the *Water-Stone Review*, *Hiram Poetry Review*, the *Evansville Review*, *Bitter Oleander*, *Santa Clara Review*, and *The Fourth River*, and has been translated into Portuguese by the University of the Azores. She is an assistant poetry editor for *Narrative Magazine*.

Jeanne Hamilton is a poet and photographer living in New York City. She is working on her first volume of poetry, to be called *Refracted Light*.

David Hovhannisyan was born in Yerevan, Armenia. He is an English major and a creative writing student at Glendale College and an introspective painter. His poetry has previously appeared in *Eclipse*.

Tyrone Jaeger's story is an excerpt from his unpublished novel *Dirty*. His work is forthcoming or appears in *The Literary Review, Exquisite Corpse, Indiana Review, Southern Humanities Review, 580 Split,* and *ONTHEBUS*. He is the Writer-in-Residence at Hendrix College in Conway, Arkansas.

Alice Jay's chapbooks are *Electric Avenue* (Finishing Line Press, 2009) and *Watermelon Moon* (Pudding House Publications, 2007). Poems appear or are forthcoming in *Oberon, Crucible, The Pinch, the new renaissance,* and *The Paterson Literary Review*.

Brad Johnson has written two chapbooks, *Void Where Prohibited* and *The Happiness Theory*. He currently serves as Poetry Editor of *Magnolia: A Florida Journal of Literary and Fine Arts*.

Catherine Johnson is a recent graduate of the English Department at California Polytechnic State University in San Luis Obispo. This is her first publication.

Rachel Kann is a James Kirkwood Award for Fiction recipient. Her poetry appears in *Word Warriors* from Seal Press. Rachel is the resident poet for daKAH Hip Hop Orchestra, an instructor for UCLA Extension Writers' Program, a DJ, and a collagist.

Brian Keenan teaches in the English Department at the University of Alaska Fairbanks, where he received an MFA in 2007 and served as editor of *Permafrost*. His fiction recently appeared in *Controlled Burn*.

Mary Beth Leymaster's short fiction has appeared in *Nimrod, Antietam Review, Snake Nation Review, Nebraska Review, South Carolina Review* and *Laurel Review*. She lives in Lancaster, Pennsylvania, where she co-founded a family business program at Elizabethtown College, and plays classical piano.

Joanne Lowery's poems have appeared in many literary magazines, including *Birmingham Poetry Review, Eclipse, Smartish Pace, Cimarron Review, roger,* and *Poetry East*. Her chapbook *Call Me Misfit* won the 2009 Frank Cat Poetry Prize. She lives in Michigan.

Jean A. McDonough earned an MFA in Creative Writing from Pacific Lutheran University at the Rainer Writing Workshop. Her poems have appeared in *Tar River Poetry, River Oak Review, American Literary Review, Excursus Literary Arts Journal, Salamander,* and *Poetry Lore*.

John McKernan is now a retired comma herder. He lives mostly in West Virginia where he edits ABZ Press. His most recent book is *Resurrection of the Dust*.

Tyler McMahon teaches fiction writing at Hawai'i Pacific University. He's the author of the novel, *How the Mistakes Were Made*.

Christopher Lee Miles lives in Fairbanks, Alaska.

Mary Carol Moran is a self-described math geek who teaches therapeutic yoga and creative writing in Auburn, Alabama. She is the author of five pseudonymous novels and two books of poetry, *Clear Soul* and *Equivocal Blessings*.

Linda Lancione Moyer writes poetry, essays, and short fiction. Her work has appeared in *Atlanta Review, CrazyHorse, The MacGuffin,*

Madison Review, Notre Dame Review, Poet Lore and *Post Road*. Her most recent chapbook is *2% Organic, 32 Short Poems from a West Marin Dairy Barn*. She lives in Berkeley, California.

Jed Myers is a Seattle-area poet whose work appears in *Golden Handcuffs Review, Atlanta Review, Prairie Schooner*, and *Fugue*. He's been editor for *Tufts Literary Magazine* and guest co-editor for *Chrysanthemum*. He's a psychiatrist with a private therapy practice and teaches at the University of Washington.

Charles Rammelkamp's most recent books include a collection of poetry, *the Book of Life,* and a collection of short fiction, *Castleman in the Academy,* both published by March Street. He also edits an online literary journal called *The Potomac.*

Bruce Douglas Reeves has published three novels, *The Night Action, Man on Fire,* and *Street Smarts,* and has completed a new novel, *Unfinished Business.* His published stories appear in *The Long Story, New Renaissance, Runner's World, Hawaii Review, Clapboard House,* and *South Carolina Review.*

Ivanov Reyez was an English professor at Odessa College. His poetry is included in *The Temple, Pinyon Poetry, Poetica: Reflections of Jewish Thought, Afterthoughts, Chili Verde Review,* and *Sierra Nevada College Review.* His short fiction has appeared in *Sephardic-American Voices: Two Hundred Years of a Literary Legacy, El Locofoco,* and *Terra Incognita.*

Suzanne Roberts' books include *Shameless* (2007), *Nothing to You* (2008), and *Plotting Temporality* (forthcoming from Red Hen Press). Her work has most recently appeared in *Fourth River, Atlanta Review,* and *National Geographic Traveler.* She currently teaches and writes in South Lake Tahoe, California.

Barbara Rockman teaches poetry at Santa Fe Community College and in private workshops. She is a graduate of Vermont College of Fine Arts' MFA in Writing Program, and her work has recently appeared in *Spoon River Review*, *Calyx*, and *Quiddity*, as well as the anthologies *Looking Back to Place* (Old School Books) and *Return of the River* (Sunstone Press). Her first collection of poetry, *Sting and Nest*, is forthcoming from Sunstone Press.

Joshua Ruffin is an MFA candidate/teaching fellow at Georgia College and State University, and a freelance music journalist whose work has appeared in the *North Coast Journal* and *Bluegrass Now*.

Amanda Skjeveland's work has recently appeared in *Flutter Poetry Journal*, *Burst*, *Literary Mama*, *Melusine*, and *Tonopah Review*. She lives in Maryland, where she teaches English and edits the literary magazine at a community college.

Leilani Squire is a creative writing student at Glendale College. She's been involved in the arts since dancing the hula on Oah'u, the island of her birth. She's published in *The Sun*, *Gentle Strength Quarterly* and *The Taylor Trust*. She facilitates a Writing Workshop at the WLA Veterans Administration and produces "Returning Soldiers Speak" where veterans read their work.

Larry Stein recently retired from a legal career with a Fortune 500 Company. He has published numerous articles in his field of employee benefits. He has B.A in history and a Juris Doctorate from U. C. Berkeley. Since retirement, he has explored his creative side through courses at Glendale College. This is his first published play.

Tanya Stepan has an MFA in poetry from Sarah Lawrence College. She lives in Rhinebeck, New York. Her work has appeared in *The South*

Carolina Review, Zone 3, Confluence, Schuylkill Valley Journal Of The Arts, Oregon East, Pearl, and *Wisconsin Review.*

Jessica Stewart is a creative writing student at Glendale College. She hopes to earn a master's degree in literature and teach English at the college level.

Johanna Stoberock's novel, *City of Ghosts,* was published by W.W. Norton in 2003. She holds an MFA from the University of Washington. Her work has appeared in numerous publications including the *Wilson Quarterly* and the *Gander Press Review.* She lives in rural Washington.

Ross Talarico's writings have appeared in *Poetry, The Atlantic, North American Review, American Poetry Review,* and *The Nation.* His books have won The Shaughnessy Prize from MLA and The Lillian Fairchild Award. He is a professor at Springfield College's San Diego campus.

Ruth Thompson has been an English professor, librarian, and college dean. She lives in a farmhouse near Buffalo, New York. She is the recipient of the *New Millennium Writings* Award, the Chautauqua Mary Jane Irion Award and the *Harpur Palate* Milton Kessler Prize. Other work has appeared in *Sonora Review, Comstock Review, New Millennium Writings, Sow's Ear Poetry Review,* and *River Styx.*

LD VanAuken's first two novels were published pseudonymously with Hachette Book Group in 2009. She is a former assistant editor of *The Literary Review.*

Gabriel Welsch is the author of *Dirt and All Its Dense Labor.* His poetry and fiction have earned honors from the Pennsylvania Arts Council Fellowship and the Thoreau Residency at the Toledo Botanical Garden. Welsch is vice president of advancement and marketing at Juniata College, and lives in Huntingdon, Pennsylvania.

Susan R. Williamson's poems have appeared in *Lumina, StorySouth, Streetlight, Three Candles, VQR,* and the *Letters to the World Anthology.* She has been a fellow at the Virginia Center for the Creative Arts and is Assistant Director of the Palm Beach Poetry Festival.

Patrice M. Wilson, PhD, has two chapbooks, *When All Else Falters* and *On Neither Side,* published by Finishing Line Press. Her work has appeared in *Bloodroot, Poiesis, Nimrod, Hawai'i Pacific Review, Hawai'i Review, Calvert Review,* and *HarpStrings.*

Maw Shein Win's writing has appeared in such journals as *Watchword, 2River, No Tell Motel, Big Bridge, Babel Fruit,* and *Moria.* She was co-founder of *Comet,* a Bay Area arts and literature journal, and an Artist-in-Residence at Headlands Center for the Arts and Can Serrat in Spain.

Steven Winn's poems have appeared in *Atlanta Review, Cape Rock, Cimarron Review, Florida Review, Poet Lore, Prairie Schooner, Southern Poetry Review,* and *Sou'wester.* His memoir, *Come Back, Como,* was published by Harper. A former Wallace Stegner Fellow at Stanford University, he lives in San Francisco.